# Manx Beetles Bugs and Butterflies

## An illustrated guide to their identification

Manx Heritage Foundation

 Stella L Thrower BSc PhD LOSc FRES

## By the same author:

Plants of Hong Kong (1971)
Hong Kong Herbs and Vines (1974)
Hong Kong Trees Volume II (1977)
An Introduction to Ecology in Hong Kong (1981)
*(co-author with I.J.Hodgkiss & S.H.Man)*
Hong Kong Climbing Plants (1984)
Hong Kong Country Parks (1984)
Hong Kong Herbs  Volume II (1984)
Hong Kong Shrubs  Volume II (1984)
Hong Kong Lichens (1988)
Hong Kong Trees, Omnibus, third Edition (1988)
Biodiversity in a Manx Churchyard (In Press)

First published by the Manx Heritage Foundation 2009
PO Box 1986, Douglas, Isle of Man IM99 1SR

www.manxheritage.com

Designed by Ruth Sutherland

Printed and bound in Wales by Gomer Press Limited, Ceredigion.

British Library Cataloguing in Publication Data
A catalogue record for this book is available from the British Library

ISBN 987-0-9554043-9-9

# Contents

# Preface

This book originated in the desire to record all the plants and animals in our garden. An ambition which is far from complete fulfilment, and indeed, will probably always be so. In addition to the butterflies recorded from the garden, at the Editor's request, nine further species are included so as to cover all the butterflies recorded from the Island.

The garden is in the south of the Island, (G.R. : SC 2950 7094); in area 0.4ha (1 acre), and was, up to the 1980's, part of a farm and either under grass or crop. We have planted trees over most of the plot which, at the time of writing, has the appearance of a small woodland. We have also a modest vegetable garden. Almost all the insects illustrated here have been found in the garden or on the walls of the house.

With the increasing interest in environmental matters and the natural world around us, it becomes ever more important to be able to make a reliable identification of insects and other living things.

The book deals with approximately 100 species of insects, most of which are very common in the south of the Island; and it seeks to provide a ready means of identifying them. There are a number of readily available books on the British insects, but unfortunately the illustrations are usually small (up to 37 species on one page in a recent publication) and the descriptive material is often slight so that a confident identification is difficult. Here, the illustrations are large and detailed, with important features emphasised; and the descriptions have been cast in a standardised form, which I believe makes it easier to compare one with another. The sequence of the descriptions within each Order follows the systematic arrangement of the Families involved, and within each Family the species are arranged alphabetically.

To make an identification using this book, the first step is to decide whether the insect belongs in one of the three Orders dealt with. Is it a beetle, bug or butterfly (including moths)? The introduction, aided by the glossary where necessary, is designed to help answer this question. Following this, the insect can be compared with the illustrations of members of that Order, with special attention being paid to its size as stated in the description. If a reasonable match is found, individual features can be checked against the description. Many of these can be seen with the naked eye, aided by the use of a x10 hand lens. Again, the glossary is designed to help with technical terms.

Identification of the specimens has been made, or confirmed, by experts in the particular group either on the Island or in Great Britain. Any errors of omission or commission are the responsibility of the author.

*February 2009*

Stella L. Thrower
Ballasalla
Isle of Man

# Acknowledgements

Mr. F. D. Bennett, 'The Crofton', Laxey, for help in obtaining specimens of mined bramble leaves.

Dr. R. L. Blackman of Canterbury, for assistance in determination of aphids.

Dr. K. Bland, National Museum of Scotland, for moth determination.

Mr. G. D. Craine, the Lepidopteran Recorder for the Isle of Man, who kindly provided a checklist of the Manx Lepidoptera.

Miss G. Douglas, Librarian, The Linnaean Society of London, for generous assistance over many years.

Mr. C. R. Guard, of The Manx Heritage Foundation, for encouragement and help in bringing the book to publication.

Ms. K. M. Hawkins, Assistant Keeper, Natural History, The Manx Museum, Douglas, for information on records of the local fauna.

Dr. K. Horstmann, for determination of ichneumonid wasp.

Dr. M. L. Luff, Department of Agricultural and Environmental Science,
The University of Newcastle, for determination of beetles.

Ms. B. Pedersen, Former Librarian, Royal Entomological Society, for generous help in obtaining references.

Dr. M. R. Shaw, Department of Natural History, Royal Museum of Edinburgh,
for determination of braconid wasps.

Mr. R. Sims, Archivist, and the staff of the Library, Manx Museum, Douglas, for the use of Library facilities and assistance in obtaining references.

Mrs. R. Sutherland, for design and layout of the book

And finally, I should like to express my heart-felt gratitude to Professor L.B.Thrower O.B.E. , my husband, without whose constant support and encouragement the project could not have been undertaken and carried out.

# Introduction

In this book 42 species of beetles,19 species of bugs and 46 species of moths and butterflies are illustrated. They form but a minute proportion of the total populations in Great Britain. Estimates vary somewhat but one authority quotes 4000 beetle species, 1630 bugs and 2400 moths and butterflies. Even so, the ones illustrated here are all common and widespread, so are very likely to be the ones seen.

## How do we recognise them?

**By their wings** Butterflies and moths are among the most conspicuous of insects, frequently seen in flight, and in many cases with handsomely patterned and coloured wings. The forewings are larger than the hindwings but both are opaque and of similar structure (I) Beetles and bugs are more often seen resting or running than flying. Both have two pairs of wings but the forewings and hindwings in both cases are very different in texture and colour. In

I    II    III    IV

beetles the forewings are hard and stiff. They are not used for flight but to form a protective cover over the delicate, transparent hindwings which are used for flight (II). Among the bugs two wing types are typical. Winged aphids, for

example, have two pairs of transparent flying wings (IV). True bugs have a forewing hardened in the basal half and transparent and membranous in the outer part. Their hindwings are again transparent and membranous (III).

**By the way they feed** Butterflies have a long, coiled, hollow tube as mouthpiece and through this they suck up liquid, usually nectar, as through a straw (V). Bugs also suck their food in liquid form by using mouthparts which are like a hypodermic needle (VII). With this they pierce the food source, plant or animal, and suck up the sap or blood. Beetles have paired biting jaws (VI), using these they can chew up solid food of various types.

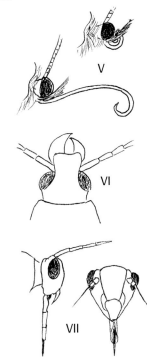

V

VI

VII

# Relationships

As soon as people became interested in the living things around them they saw that, firstly there were immense numbers of different living things, and secondly that they must have some sort of framework or system to refer to them if they were not to be hopelessly confused. One obvious distinction is between animals and plants, so there is a plant kingdom and an animal kingdom, and the insects are members of the animal kingdom. Another distinction is between animals with backbones which support them, the vertebrates; and animals without backbones, many of which rely on a rigid outer surface for support. These are the invertebrates, and insects belong in this group.

The insects dealt with in this book fall into 37 families. A selection of these shows how the classification works, as follows:

A Family contains individuals which are clearly related, for example the beetles in the Family Coccinellidae are all obviously ladybirds. Individuals within a Family differ in small ways, and some are more closely related than others. Based on the closeness or otherwise of these relationships a Family is divided into a number of genera and each genus into species.

For example, within the butterfly Family Pieridae, is the genus *Pieris*, which contains the three species illustrated: *Pieris brassicae* - the large white, *Pieris napi* - the green-veined white and *Pieris rapae* - the small white.

The species is defined as a group of individuals which can interbreed.

## Class
Insecta
(animals with
6 legs)

### Order
Coleoptera
(beetles)

#### Family
Silphidae - carrion beetles
Elateridae - click beetles
Coccinellidae - ladybirds
Curculionidae - weevils

### Order
Hemiptera
(bugs)

#### Family
Aphididae - aphids
Cicadellidae - plant hoppers
Miridae - capsid bugs
Anthocoridae - flower bugs

### Order
Lepidoptera
(moths and
butterflies)

#### Family
Tineidae - clothes moths
Oecophoridae - house moths
Pterophoridae - plume moths
Pieridae - white butterflies

# Beetles - Order Coleoptera

Insects with two pairs of wings, the forewings hard and leathery, meeting along the mid-line of the dorsal surface. Hindwings membranous and concealed beneath the forewings. Prothorax large and mobile. Mouthparts always of the biting type.

## Suborder Adephaga

Hind coxae immovably fixed to the body and completely dividing the first visible abdominal sternite. Antennae with 11 segments, usually filiform or moniliform.

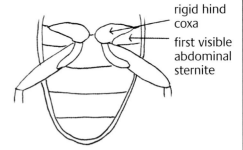

rigid hind coxa

first visible abdominal sternite

## Suborder Polyphaga

Hind coxae usually movably fixed to the body and very rarely dividing the first visible abdominal sternite. Antennae various.

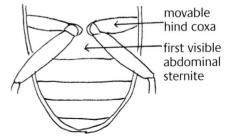

movable hind coxa

first visible abdominal sternite

# Beetles - Order Coleoptera

## Suborder Adephaga

## Suborder Polyphaga

## Superfamily Staphylinoidea   26

# Ground and Tiger Beetles - Family Carabidae

The Carabidae belong to the suborder Adephaga, which is characterised by filiform antennae, 5-segmented tarsi and backward-projecting hind coxae (C). Fig. I. A terrestrial family, the members of which are mostly predatory. The thread-like antennae (A) are inserted at the side of the head between the eyes and mandibles (M), or above the base of the mandibles. The wing cases (elytra) meet at the centre line and cover most or all of the abdomen. The segments of the tarsi are five on all legs, and the hind tarsal segments are simple, never lobed. Hind trochanters (T) are large, always longer than the diameter of the femur (F) , and clearly visible. Lengths from 2-30mm. Two subfamilies, considered by some authors as two families.

## Ground Beetles - Subfamily Carabinae

Wing-cases usually dark brown or black, especially in the larger species, and may have a metallic shine, usually striate. The eyes are not markedly protuberant (Fig. II) and the antennae (A) are inserted on the side of the head, under the side margin of the temple, between the eyes and the mandibles (M). The head, at the level of the eyes, almost always narrower than the pronotum (P)

## Tiger Beetles - Subfamily Cicindelinae

Wing-cases metallic green or brown, often with whitish cross-bars, not striate. Eyes conspicuously protruding (Fig. III) and the antennae (A) inserted on the temple in front of the eye and above the base of the mandibles (M). Head at eye level as wide as, or wider than the pronotum (P).

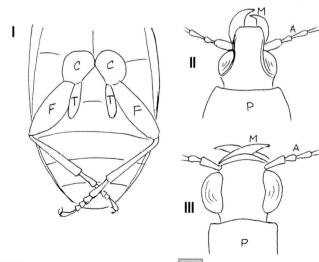

# Black Garden Ground Beetle, Strawberry Beetle

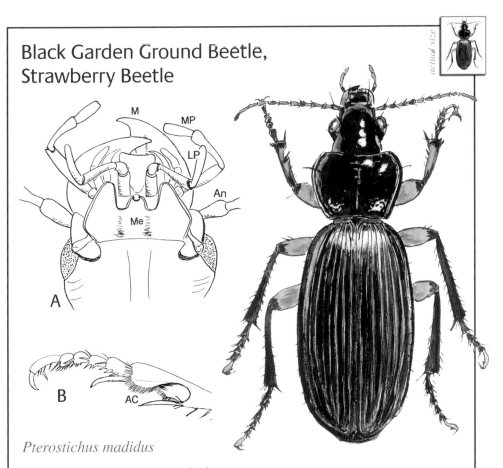

A

B    AC

*Pterostichus madidus*

A very common, large black, wingless beetle; the legs variably coloured, they may be black or reddish as illustrated. Found in open country, gardens, and cultivated areas, particularly those which are used for soft- fruit crops.

The black garden ground beetle likes to eat fruit, and is thus an unwelcome visitor, particular to strawberry growing fields, as the common name implies.

*Body length 13 - 17mm*

**A:**  underside of head
    An: base of antenna
    LP: labial palp
    MP: maxillary palp
    Me: mentum
    M:   mandible
**B:**  foreleg tarsus and end of tibia
    AC: antenna cleaner

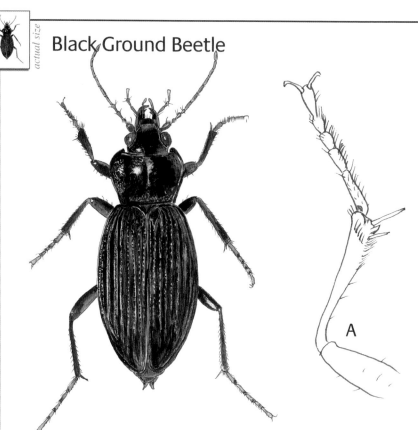

# Black Ground Beetle

*actual size*

*Nebria brevicollis*

A common species in Britain, in fact the commonest ground beetle in the garden. Unlike most of its close relatives (other *Nebria* species) which are coastal, it lives far away from water in woodlands and gardens. It does, however, like damp places with plenty of leaf mould.

The adult beetles emerge in early Summer and eat greedily for 2-3 weeks, after which they gather together in groups of up to 80 insects, find a safe place under a stone or log and go into a dormant state, living on the fat laid down in the feeding period.

In October they awaken and begin to lay eggs, continuing in this activity up to April of the following year

*Body length 10 – 13mm*
**A:** ventral view of foreleg

# Common Ground Beetle

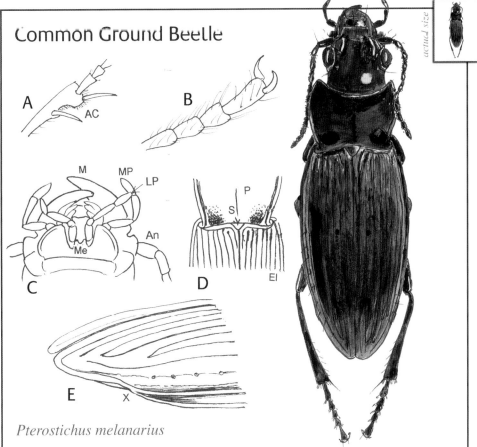

*actual size*

A: AC

B

C: M MP LP An Me

D: P S El

E: X

*Pterostichus melanarius*

The common ground beetle is black, wingless and unable to fly, but it can run very fast and has been measured to run at the rate of 1 metre in 8 seconds. It is locally common in open country, fields and gardens, and usually seen in July and August, when eggs are laid. The larvae developing from these eggs overwinter.

The main food is caterpillars and it is reputed to be able to eat up to three times its body weight of caterpillars in a day, when it has the chance! It also will eat seeds and fruit, and like its close relative already described, can become a pest of strawberries.

*Body length 12 - 18mm*

**A:** foreleg tarsus and end of tibia
   AC: antenna cleaner
**B:** last four segments of the tarsus showing the typical hairs on the underside
**C:** underside of the head
   An: base of antenna
   LP: labial palp
   MP: maxillary palp
   M: mandible
   Me: mentum
**D:** hind part of the pronotum (P), elytral bases (El) and scutellum (S)
**E:** tip of the elytra (wing-case) showing the crossed margin (X)

# Dark Beetle

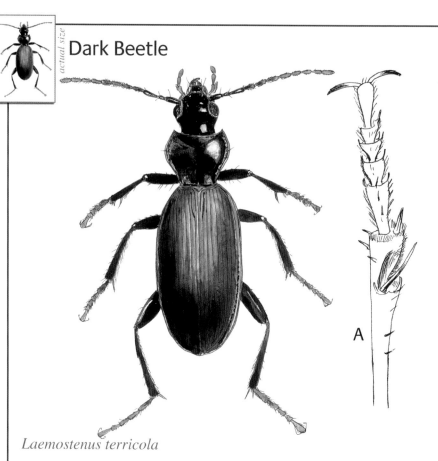

*Laemostenus terricola*

This beetle gets its common name from its preference for dark places, both adults and larvae may be found in cellars, stables and other out-buildings as well as under stones, in mines, caves and rabbit burrows.

It is widespread, but nowhere very common; active from April to September, breeding in the Autumn. No information has been found with respect to its eating habits or other activities.

*Body length 15mm*

**A:** foreleg tarsus and end of tibia, which has a single spur at the tip, and, just back from the tip, the notch which is specialised as an antenna cleaner

# Ditch Beetle

actual size

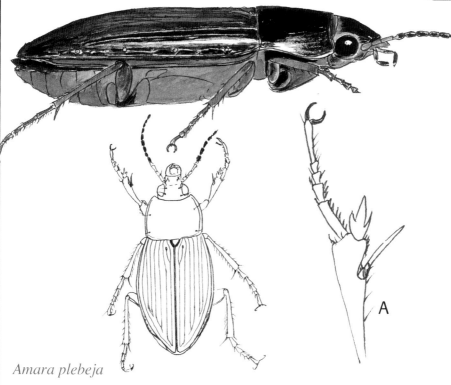

*Amara plebeja*

A

**A:** foreleg tibia and tarsus showing the three-pronged spur at the end of the tibia, which is characteristic of this beetle

Ditch beetles are common and some 30 different ones are found in Britain. Unfortunately, while it is rather easy to say whether a beetle is one of the ditch beetles, it is much more of a problem to say which one it is.

The one illustrated is the commonest, and one of the smallest, with a three-pointed spur on the end of the middle joint of the foreleg. It lives in grassland, farm fields and road margins, hiding under stones and fallen leaves, and venturing out when the sun shines. It eats a mixed diet including insect larvae and plants, often it is seen on grasses and other plants eating their seeds.

The ditch beetle overwinters in grass tussocks along field margins, reappearing and starting to breed when Spring comes.

*Body length 6 - 8mm*

# Ditch Beetle

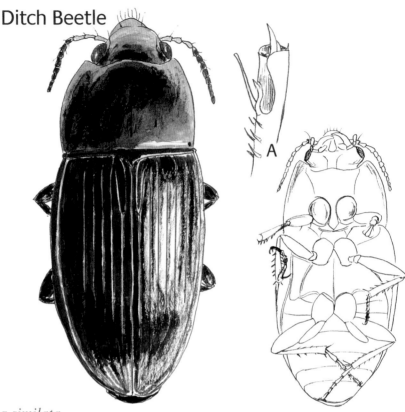

**A**

*Amara similata*

This ditch beetle is larger than the previous one (*A. plebeja*), but otherwise very similar. One essential difference is that the spur on the end of the middle joint (the tibia) of the front leg has only a single point in this beetle.

It is generally found in much drier places than *A. plebeja*, and in these habitats it is quite common.

With both of these ditch beetles the colour may vary, often it is a light bluish green or coppery colour as well as black like the ones illustrated. This one was found in the garden, on vegetables.

*Body length 8 - 10mm*

**A:** end of the tibia of the foreleg showing the more usual single-pointed spur at its tip

20

# Flat Ground Beetle

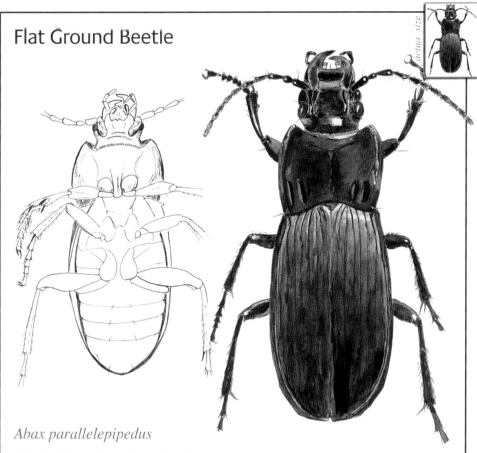

*Abax parallelepipedus*

This black beetle was found under a stone in the garden and this is a typical habitat. It is common in woodland and gardens under fallen leaves, soil debris or stones, always in moist and shady situations. It runs about and hunts its food on the ground as, unlike many other beetles, it has no wings under the wing cases, and so cannot fly.

The flat beetle is a carnivore, a predator on soft-bodied invertebrates such as slugs and earthworms which it crunches up and swallows without first pouring out digestive juice on them and predigesting them as do many similar beetles.

*Body length 18 - 20mm*

BEETLES

# Krummhorn Beetle

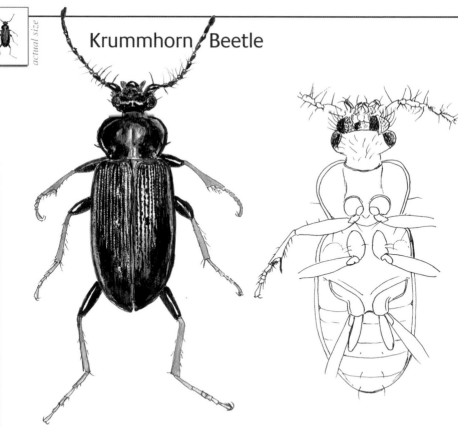

*Loricera pilicornis*

The Krummhorn beetle is unique among British beetles because of the long, dark bristles on the lower segments of the antennae, near the mouth. These bristles are used to help in capturing and holding its prey which consists of small creatures such as mites and springtails.

Most other related carnivorous beetles can bring their digestive juices up into the mouth so they can digest their prey before swallowing it.

The Krummhorn beetle, on the other hand, cannot do this, it tears its food apart and eats the fragments whole. It is a common beetle, found usually in damp places, wet swampy ground, and near water. It hibernates in Winter, often many in a group together, under stones or in leaf litter.

*Body length 7mm*

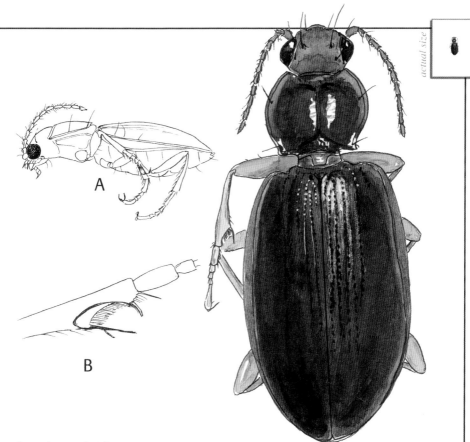

A

B

## *Ocys harpaloides*

Widely distributed throughout Britain, found under bark, or stones on moist clay soil. Some immature adults have been observed in the nest of a jay in England. Otherwise  little information on its life style is available.

Spring and early Summer are the most likely times to see this beetle. It hibernates as an adult throughout the Winter.

*Body length 4 - 6mm*

**A:** lateral view of beetle
**B:** tip of the tibia of the foreleg with antenna cleaning notch

actual size

# Common Speed Swimmer, Diving Beetle

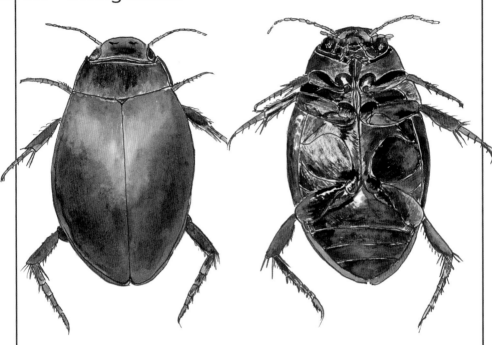

*Agabus bipustulatus*

Very widespread and common in ponds and stagnant water.

True water beetles belong to two groups: the first, to which the diving beetle belongs, are carnivores, swim by moving the opposite legs of each pair together, and get their oxygen by tilting their tail end up and trapping a bubble of air under the wing cases. The other group feeds on both plants and animals, swims by moving their legs alternately, and obtains oxygen by raising the front end to trap a bubble of air under the thorax.

The diving beetle larvae are also predators, and can be found at most times of the year. They spend most of their time running about on the bed of the pond, coming up to the surface for air by climbing up a plant stem.

*Body length  8 - 11mm*

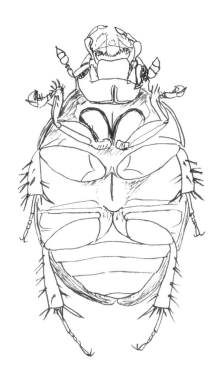

## *Sphaeridium scarabaeoides*

*Sphaeridium* is an oddity in that it belongs in the family of water scavenger beetles but it is a dry-land insect, living principally in horse or cow dung. It digs galleries and passages through the dung as it feeds on the undigested plant remains in it. As it feeds it also takes in the eggs of parasitic worms. Cattle eat many of these beetles as they graze, and thus become infected with the parasites contained in the beetle's gut.

Female beetles lay their eggs into wet dung, but they have the problem of preventing the eggs from getting too wet. This they can do because they possess a spinning apparatus similar to that of spiders. They use the web they spin to weave a loose silk protective cover for the eggs. The larvae which hatch from these eggs feed on fly larvae in the dung

*Body length 5 - 6.5mm*

# Superfamily Staphylinoidea

A very large group of mainly predatory beetles, all more than 7mm long and most with short wing-cases (elytra) which allow at least three of the abdominal segments to be seen. Hindwings are present, but when the insect is not in flight they are folded and hidden under the elytra. The antennae have 10 or 11 segments and may be filiform or clubbed. If they are clubbed, the club is symmetrical. The number of segments in the tarsi of fore, mid and hind legs is 5:5:5; some of the segments, but never all, may be lobed.

The superfamily Staphylinoidea contains, as well as a number of small and specialised families, the burying beetles (family Silphidae), family Leiodidae, and the enormous family of rove beetles (family Staphylinidae).

## Burying beetles and Carrion beetles - Family Silphidae

Members of this family are scavengers, feeding on decaying organic matter and some are well-known for their habit of burying carcases.

The body outline is a broad oval and the antennae are usually clubbed, with the club formed of the four last segments. The antennae are never elbowed, and the first antennal segment is only as long as the second and third segments together.

Ocelli are absent from the vertex of the head, which is often constricted like a neck behind the eyes. The head is much narrower than the thorax or pronotum, which has rounded sides and is, at base, about as wide as the wing-cases. These are shortened to show at most three segments of the tip of the abdomen. In the forelegs, the coxae are typically cone-shaped and projecting. Body length is 9-20mm.

## Family Leiodidae

The antennae have eleven segments and terminate in a very obvious club of four or more segments, this club is never one-sided, toothed or leaf-like. The elytra are arched and more or less semi-circular in section. They are not shortened and so cover the whole abdomen. Tarsi are never lobed, and the number of segments is variable, the tarsal formula may be 5:5:5; 5:5:4; 5:3:3 or 4:3:3.

# Black Snail Hunter

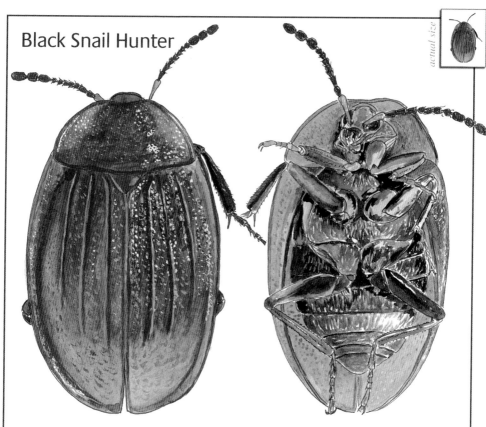

*Silpha atrata*

Despite the common name, this fairly large beetle comes in a variety of shades of brown and black, the one illustrated was brown.

The snail hunter lives in damp and shady places, sometimes in moss or under bark, but most often in places where it is likely to find its favourite food, a snail. The beetle has quite a sharp narrow head (in the illustration the head is tucked under the hard outer prothorax). It is able to use its head as a tool, either to break open a snail shell, or to push right down into the shell to reach the snail and eat it.

*Body length 11 - 15mm*

# Red-Banded Sexton Beetle

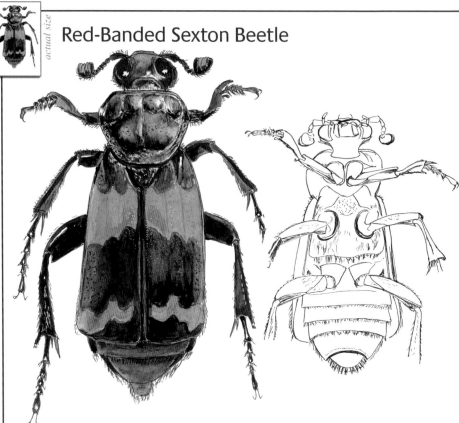

*actual size*

*Nicrophorus investigator*

Sometimes called burying beetles. They do a useful job in clearing up small corpses from the countryside. Both males and females work together. They have scent detectors on their antennae which help them to find dead animals. When they find one, such as a mouse or small bird, they dig out a hole beneath it and drag it into the hole so that it is buried.

The female then lays her eggs near the corpse and the young larvae and their parents use it as a food source. They also feed on the maggots and other scavengers which find their way to the corpse. The beetles show a deal of parental care of their young and communicate with them by a series of chirping noises. When the larvae are fully grown, they make their way into the soil below to pupate. Adults are seen in Spring and Summer, flying mostly in the night-time.

It is typical of the Sexton beetle's family that the wing-cases are shorter than the abdomen so the tail-end segments can be seen.

*Body length 17mm*

# Sexton Beetle

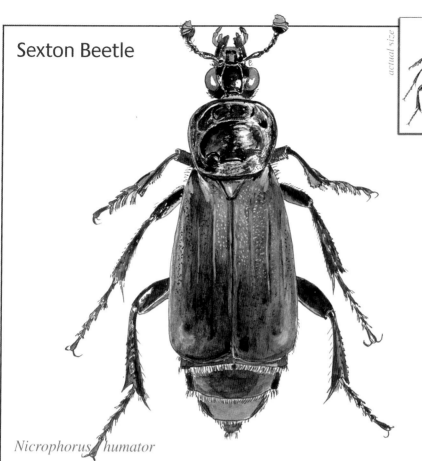

*Nicrophorus humator*

Sometimes called burying beetles. They do a useful job in clearing up small corpses from the countryside. Both males and females work together. They have scent detectors on their antennae which help them to find dead animals. When they find one, such as a mouse or small bird, they dig out a hole beneath it and drag it into the hole so that it is buried.

The female then lays her eggs near the corpse and the young larvae and their parents use it as a food store. They also feed on the maggots and other scavengers which find their way to the corpse. The beetles show a deal of parental care of their young and communicate with them by a series of chirping noises. When the larvae are fully grown, they make their way into the soil below to pupate. Adults are seen in Spring and Summer, flying mostly in the night-time.

It is typical of the Sexton beetle's family that the wing-cases are shorter than the abdomen so the tail-end segments can be seen.

*Body length 24mm*

*actual size*

# Globular Fungus Beetle

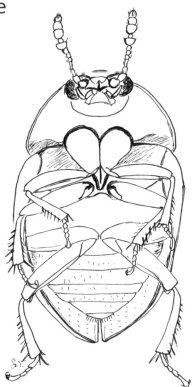

*Leiodes calcarata*

Active from mid-Summer to about
October, in woodland and gardens.
The legs have strong spines and are
adapted for digging. This is important
as the beetle feeds on fungi in the soil.
Globular fungus beetles often gather
together in woodland clearings or
beside water where they swarm from
half an hour before sunset to half an
hour afterwards

*Body length  2 - 3.5mm*

BEETLES

# Rove Beetles - Family Staphylinidae

The major family within the Superfamily Staphylinoidea which is characterised by the presence of elytra which are short, exposing one or more of the abdominal segments, hence, short-winged beetles. The antennae are rarely clubbed and if they are so, the club is never one-sided. The tarsi never have lobed segments.

Staphylinidae is an extremely large family, all members of which have short wing-cases (elytra) which leave at least three of the abdominal segments exposed. Beneath the elytra there is usually a pair of well developed wings which are folded in a complex way to fit beneath the short elytra.

Classification within the family has presented a problem, which different authors have solved in different ways, and in particular there are differences between the accepted British system and that of the Central European authors. Unwin (1984) gives the numbers for British beetles as 975 species in 188 genera, thus subdivision into smaller groups with related characters is a necessity if only for ease of handling such an enormous number.

The recent grouping of Stresemann (2000) defines the Family Staphylinidae as those beetles with the elytra so short as to leave more than 3 abdominal segments visible, the elytral suture straight, the abdomen of 8 segments, and the antennae usually of 11 segments. He subdivides the family into 17 subfamilies, two of which are represented here.

## Subfamily Tachyporinae

Insects less than 12mm long. Antennae with 11 segments, and inserted outside the base of the mandibles. Head with small temples and sloping cheeks, the vertex lacking ocelli. The head sunk in the pronotum, hiding the temples, and anterior femorae scarcely visible from above. Body more or less boat-shaped with the abdomen narrowed from base to apex. Wing-cases so short that at least four abdomen segments are visible. Tarsi with 4 or 5 segments.

# Rove Beetles - Family Staphylinidae

## Subfamily Staphylininae

Insects of 3-30mm. Antennae 11-segmented, inserted at the front of the head inside the bases of the mandibles, more distant from one another than from the eyes. Head with distinct temples and short cheeks. Abdomen generally rather flat with upturned side margins, apically with long styles. Subdivided into three tribes, which can be distinguished as in the following key:

### Key to tribes

1a Wing-cases somewhat curved and overlapping each other at the suture.
Tribe Xantholinini

1b Wing-cases meeting each other along a straight line..........2

2a Length 2.8-14mm. Antennae arising with the distance between them exactly the same as their distance from the eyes. First segment of the hind foot scarcely longer than the second.
Tribe Othiini

2b Length 3-32mm. Antennae arising more distant from each other than they are from the eyes. First segment of the hind foot often lengthened.
Tribe Staphylinini

Both Joy (1932) and Freude et al (1964) also separate Tribe Quediini, and distinguish it from Staphylinini as follows:

Quediini: Thorax with a few scattered large punctures, never more than three on each side, and all in the front half. Epipleura (side margins) of the pronotum not visible from the side. Head below the eyes with a marginal ridge. Abdomen often tapering.

Staphylinini: Thorax punctured throughout or almost so, or with a row of at least three large punctures on each side, some in the hinder half. Epipleura (side margins) of the pronotum visible from the side at least in the hind half. Head below the eyes with no marginal ridge. Abdomen usually parallel-sided.

In the following pages species of *Ocypus*, *Philonthus* and *Quedius* (Tribe Staphylinini) and *Xantholinus* (Tribe Xantholinini) are described.

# Devil's Coach Horse

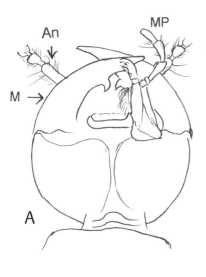

*Ocypus olens*

One of the largest of the short-winged beetles, widespread and common in gardens, woodland and open country, where it hides under stones or fallen wood by day. Sometimes it comes into houses hunting for its prey. It feeds on small insects, slugs and worms. It has powerful jaws, some 3mm long which are capable of giving a painful bite.

When the beetle feels threatened, it bends up its tail so that it looks like a scorpion, an action intended to scare off any enemies such as insect-eating birds and small mammals

*actual size*

*Body length 22 - 32mm*

**A:** head from below
   **M:** mandible
   **MP:** maxillary palp
   **An:** basal segments of antenna

Note: labial palps, maxilla and maxillary palp have been removed from the left side to show the characteristic tooth on the inner side of the mandible.

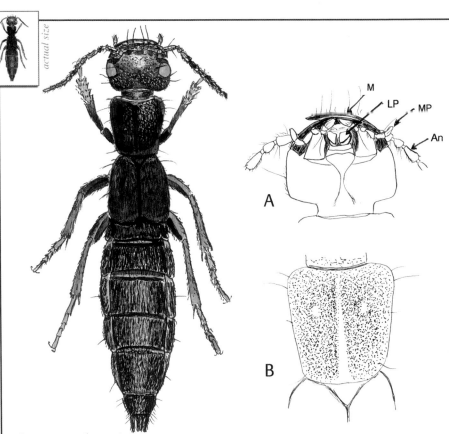

*actual size*

A
M: mandible
LP: labial palp
MP maxillary palp
An: basal segments of antenna

B

## Ocypus melanarius

A common member of the family which typically have very short wing-cases, so that segments of the abdomen are visible. Despite the short wing-cases, many of these beetles have quite well developed wings folded up under the wing-cases and they are well able to fly.

*O. melanarius* is common in the ground litter in woodland, where it feeds on insects and insect larvae, worms and slugs. It is clearly smaller than the closely related devil's coach horse (see previous page) and its feet are often a reddish brown compared with the completely black feet of its relative. As far as can be discovered, it does not adopt the same threatening postures.

The beetle illustrated was collected from a pitfall trap in the garden.

*Body length 13 - 20mm*

A:  head from below
    M: mandible
    LP: labial palp
    MP maxillary palp
    An: basal segments of antenna

B: dorsal view of pronotum showing the pattern of punctuation.

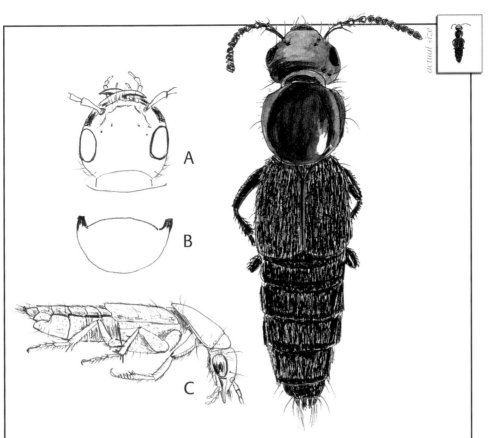

*actual size*

## *Philonthus laminatus*

*Philonthus* is a very large genus with many species. This beetle lives in decaying fungi, dung, or moss in Winter, and is one of the commonest beetles found in the dung of herbivorous animals.

One way of telling these very similar short-winged beetles apart is by observing the punctures on the upper part of the back (on the thorax, or pronotum). This species is unusual in lacking any such punctures, compared with the other two relatives described (*P. marginatus* and *P. varius*)

*Body length 8 - 11mm*

**A:** head from above
**B:** section of abdomen to show the ridges along the sides
**C:** side view of beetle

## *Philonthus marginatus*

Another species which lives in
decaying vegetable matter and dung.
This species has four punctures on
each side of the thorax, and also the
useful feature of orange-coloured side
margins to the thorax, and yellowish
legs (legs of the other species are
black).

*Body length 7 - 9mm*

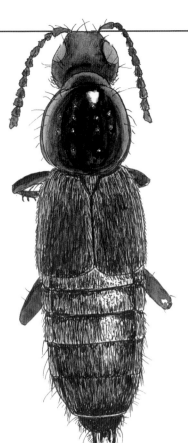

## Philonthus varius

*P. varius* is another black species. It is smaller than *P. laminatus* and a careful look reveals four punctures on each side of the thorax. *P. laminatus* was collected in the garden, but both *P. marginatus* and *P. varius* were collected inside the house.

*Body length 5.5mm*

B

A

## Quedius curtipennis

*Quedius* is an extremely large genus with 49 species in the British Isles. The beetle illustrated is a common and widespread member, but quite inconspicuous. Little information on it could be found.

Members of the genus *Quedius* are found in leaf litter, in moss, under bark, in compost heaps, and many in the nests of small animals such as moles. Insects, such as these, which inhabit the nests of small animals or birds are often thought to have a useful function in eating up the rubbish and debris of the nest. The beetle illustrated was caught in a pitfall trap in the garden.

*Body length 17mm*

**A:** head and upper part of pronotum, from above
**B:** side view of beetle

BEETLES

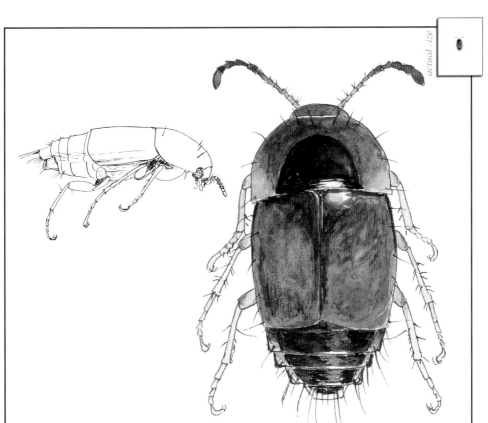

actual size

## *Tachyporus hypnorum*

This little beetle is also in the family which typically has short wing cases, so that one can see the tail-end of its abdomen. It is quite common in Spring and Winter, and lives in leafy litter on the ground, in mossy places and in compost heaps.

There is not much information available about *Tachyporus* so if you see one it is a good idea to look at it closely and see what it is doing, then make your own notes about it, perhaps even trying to invent a good common name (If you do so, I should be glad to hear about it.).

*Body length  3 - 4mm*

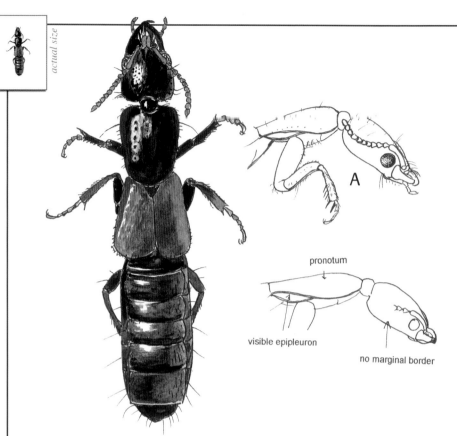

A

pronotum

visible epipleuron

no marginal border

## *Xantholinus glabratus*

*Xantholinus* species are found in decaying plant litter, leaves, moss and under stones. Most of them are common, but there is little information readily available about them. To first sight they appear similar to *Philonthus* and *Quedius* but closer inspection and comparison shows that the antennae are closer together and the head is much the same width as the thorax at the shoulder.

*X. glabratus* is the only species of this genus found in dung, where its orange wing-cases make it quite conspicuous. The specimen illustrated was collected from garden soil.

*Body length 10 - 14mm*

**A:** side view of head, pronotum and foreleg. Relevant labelling on lower diagram

# Dung Beetle

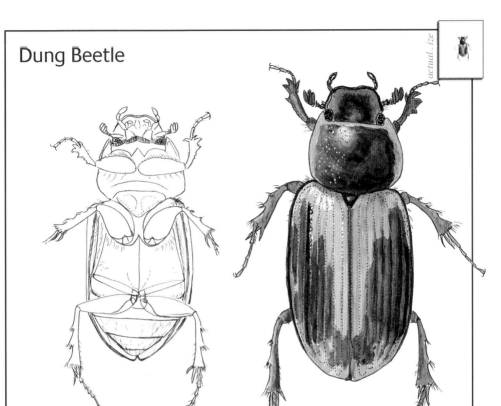

*actual size*

*Aphodius prodromus*

A very common day-flying dung beetle found throughout Great Britain, mainly in dung but also occasionally in rotting vegetation. It has a definite preference for horse dung but will use some others if necessary, with the exception of cow manure which it appears to dislike.

The adult beetles are in flight from April to July. They lay their eggs directly into the dung which forms the food for the larvae. Overwintering adults have been found in plant litter and in flood debris, between November and March.

The genus *Aphodius* has 41 species in Great Britain, and over 1000 worldwide. It is considered to be possibly the largest animal genus.

*Body length 4 - 7mm*

# Soldier Beetle

*actual size*

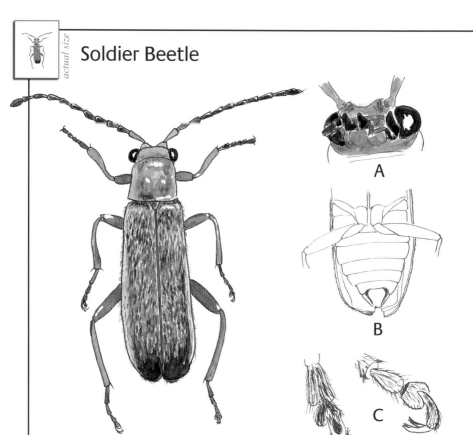

A

B

C

*Rhagonycha fulva*

A common insect of the roadside and meadow flora, from the end of June to August or September. The adult beetles are predators and often seen in numbers on flowers of hawthorn and umbellifers such as hogweed and wild carrot. A curious feature is that mating pairs are often common, as mating takes a long time.

The beetles are very active in the sunshine, but it has been noted that some hours before the outbreak of a storm the beetles all retreat to a protected position on the underside of the leaves. The larvae are also predatory, and live in the soil.

*Body length 7 - 10mm*

**A:** head from below, showing dark inner labial palps and dark outer maxillary palps, the end section of these palps is widened and more or less triangular
**B:** abdomen from below
**C:** terminal segments of the foot (tarsus) of the middle leg from below and from the side to show the forked claws

BEETLES

# Click Beetle, Skipjack

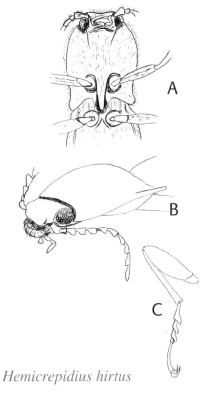

A

B

C

*Hemicrepidius hirtus*

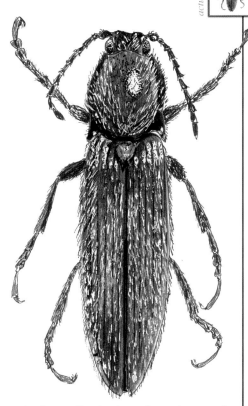

The click beetle is common from May to July in bushy undergrowth. These beetles can jump a distance many times their own length, giving a distinctly heard "click" as they do so – hence one of the common names.

On the underside of the thorax there is a pointed peg which fits into a slot in the segment behind it. This acts somehow as a spring by which the beetle is catapulted into the air, but the exact way in which the mechanism works is still not completely understood. The function of the action is thought to be either to frighten or evade an enemy.

The larvae live in the soil, are long and worm-like, and are known as wire-worms. They feed on plant roots and can become serious garden pests.

*Body length 10 - 14mm*

**A:** underside of thorax to show "peg and slot" jumping mechanism
**B:** upper surface of head and thorax
**C:** hind leg

# Australian Spider Beetle

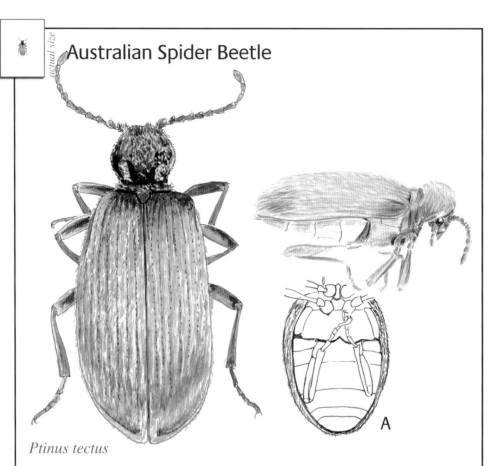

*Ptinus tectus*

This little beetle is a come-over, arriving in Europe from Australia about 1900. It has spread widely and is now very common. Because of the long, spindly legs and hairy surface they are thought to look somewhat like a spider, hence its common name.

It is always found with stored products, particularly foods. The female may lay up to 1000 eggs and development from the egg to larva and adult takes about 3 months. Both adult and larva feed on grain, flour, dried fruits and other dried foodstuffs. The beetle illustrated was found in a flour bin. As well as stored foodstuffs the adults eat a wide range of items such as textiles, insect collections and stuffed animals, they can thus be a serious pest not only in the home, factory or warehouse but also in museums and universities which hold reference collections of plants and animals.

*Body length 4mm*

**A:** underside of abdomen

# Superfamily Cucujoidea

Antennae (A) filiform, relatively short and fine, ending in a club which is symmetrical and never one-sided. End segment of the maxillary palps (P) flattened and axe-shaped. The head, and at least part of the eye visible from above. Elytra never short but covering the abdomen completely or almost so. Tarsi with four segments (tarsal formula 4:4:4 but seemingly 3:3:3 as the small third segment is hidden in the lobed second segment).

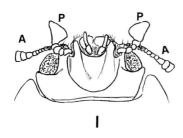

**I**

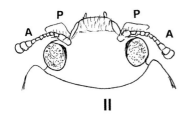

**II**

I:   Head from below to show antennae (A) and maxillary palps (P)
II:   Head from above

## Ladybirds - Family Coccinellidae

Small beetles, less than 10mm long; convex, with oval or hemispherical body shape. Antennae with the end three segments thickened to form a small club.(A) Antennal sockets close to the inner margin of the eyes. Mandibles large, the maxillary palps four-segmented with the end segment axe-shaped (P). Pronotum broader than long and extending forward at the front margins. Elytra smooth, lacking longitudinal grooves. Abdomen with 5-7 obvious segments, the first with a humped central area. Legs retractable into hollows beneath the body. Tarsi with two claws which may be simple or divided.

## Family Byturidae

Antennae with 11 segments, the terminal three forming a symmetrical club. Pronotum length at most two-thirds of the width, surface smooth, sides rounded with flattened margins. Wing cases covering most of the abdomen, without ribs or clear rows of punctures. Abdomen with 5 (rarely 4) visible segments. Fore leg coxae not projecting, more or less oblique. Coxae of hind legs flat, not excavated. Tarsi with 4 segments, the segments more or less equally long, the second and third with hairy lobes. The whole beetle a rich yellow colour and covered with a fine yellow pubescence.

# 7-Spot Ladybird

*Coccinella 7-punctata*

A very common and familiar insect, found in most gardens and many other habitats. It is a welcome guest as it feeds on a wide variety of aphids, which otherwise may become pests. The beetle lays its eggs in June and these hatch after about four days. The larvae also feed on aphids for some four to five weeks before they pupate. The adult beetles emerge in the Autumn and overwinter in sheltered positions, often near the ground, and often many together.

When they are disturbed, ladybirds give out a yellowish, strong-smelling liquid with a bitter taste which deters many predators. Unfortunately for the ladybird, spiders, birds and ants do not seem to be deterred by it.

*Body length 6.5mm*

# 11-Spot Ladybird

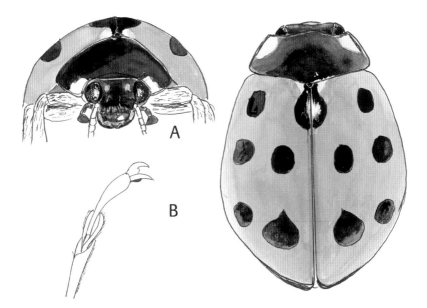

A

B

*Coccinella 11-punctata*

The 11-spot ladybird is found mostly in the south and east of the British Isles, in various places but mainly near the coast.

Both adults and larvae feed on aphids which they pre-digest. The ladybird coughs up digestive fluid on the prey and can thus suck in the digested prey in semi-liquid form. With the approach of Winter the ladybirds feed actively so that they have enough stored food to last them over the Winter period during which they hibernate. They select suitable Winter quarters in September and October, and gather together in groups which often contain a mixture of 11-spot, 2-spot and 14-spot ladybirds.

In extreme Winters many may die of cold, so perhaps with global warming we may see more ladybirds surviving into the second year.

*Body length 5 - 6mm*

**A:** view from front
**B:** foot (Note: both claws of the foot are toothed, the upper one, viewed from the side, shows the tooth, in the lower one, viewed from above, the tooth is hidden.)

# Raspberry Beetle

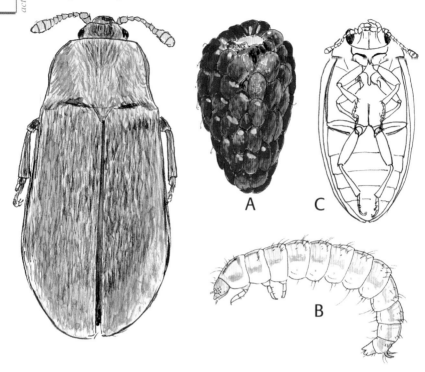

A   C

B

*Byturus tomentosus*

During May to July adult beetles may be seen, firstly feeding on the flowers of hawthorn and other fruit trees, then, when the raspberry is in flower, feeding on its buds and blossoms.

The beetle lays its eggs in the raspberry flowers. These eggs hatch in about ten days and the larvae feed on the developing raspberry fruit, becoming fully grown in about five weeks. If a raspberry fruit shows a dark patch at the top, as in the illustration, it will contain one of these larvae.

When the larva is fully grown, it migrates to the soil below the bush to pupate. It overwinters as a pupa in the soil and the adult beetles will emerge in the next Spring.

*Body length of beetle 4mm*
*Body length of larva 7mm*

**A:** raspberry fruit showing black area near the top indicating the present of the beetle larva within
**B:** beetle larva
**C:** underside of beetle

# Woolly-Hair Beetle

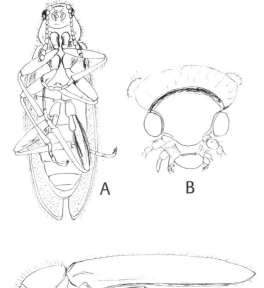

A

B

C

*Psilothrix cyaneus*

This beetle is a "come-over", found
normally in the coastal regions of
England, Wales and Ireland on dunes
and grasslands. The specimen
illustrated was discovered in an English
lettuce which was purchased locally.
The adult beetles are usually seen on
flowers of hawkweeds; the larvae live
under the bark of trees.

*Body length 6mm*

**A:** underside of beetle
**B:** head, viewed from the front
**C:** lateral view of beetle

# Superfamily Chrysomeloidea

Plant feeders, antennae with no distinct club, tarsi all apparently three-segmented, the fourth segment being very small. (See below).

## Leaf Beetles - Family Chrysomelidae

Mostly rounded beetles with shiny, often coloured elytra. The first joint of the antennae is mostly stronger than the following joints, the end joints not specially developed.

The head is mostly retracted under the pronotum up to the eyes, which are round in shape. The hind margin of the pronotum is rounded.

Tibia with usually one spine, the third tarsal segment expanded to conceal, or almost conceal, the minute fourth segment.

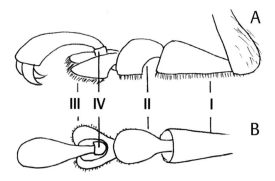

**Tarsus**
**A:** lateral view
**B:** from above
**I, II, III, IV:** first, second, third and fourth tarsal segments

# Leaf Beetle

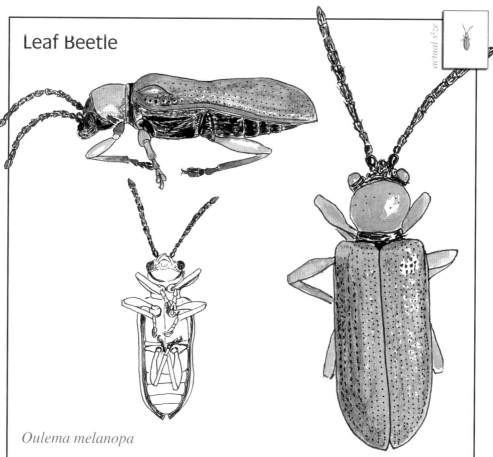

*Oulema melanopa*

On sunny days in Spring this brightly coloured little beetle will often be found basking in the sun, frequently on the outer walls of houses. It lives in grassy places such as gardens and fields, and feeds on grass leaves. These can include the leaves of cereal crops such as wheat, barley or oats but apparently it never does enough damage to be considered as a pest.

Some other related leaf beetles have the habit of swarming in large numbers and such a swarm may completely defoliate plants; a beetle such as the asparagus leaf beetle can in this way become a serious pest.

*Body length  4.5mm*

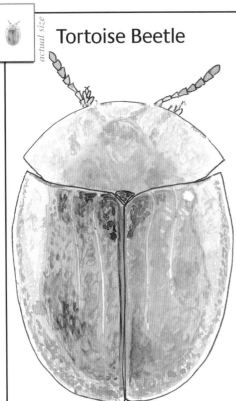

*actual size*

# Tortoise Beetle

*Cassida rubiginosa*

All the tortoise beetles are green and have a flat, wide body beneath which they can draw in their legs and head. The green colour typically fades after death, so that in life the beetle illustrated would have been a brighter green.

They are fairly common and found on thistles, burdock plants and other plants of the same family, where their green colour forms a good camouflage. Beetles in this family make an egg-case attached to the underside of a leaf, in which they lay 6-10 eggs in May/June; these will hatch in 1-2 weeks depending on the temperature. The larvae developing from these eggs are up to

9mm long, spiny, and with a structure like a sharp fork on the tail end which bends forward over its back. This holds the excreta and moulted skins so that it forms a protective umbrella and looks like bird droppings, hiding the larva from its enemies.

The larva feeds on the same plants as the adult and finally pupates within the stem. Adults emerge from June to September and overwinter in plant litter.

*Body length 6 - 8mm*

BEETLES

actual size

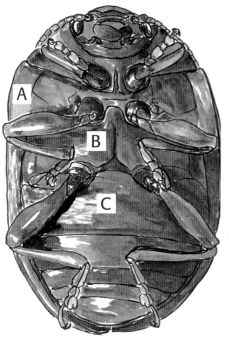

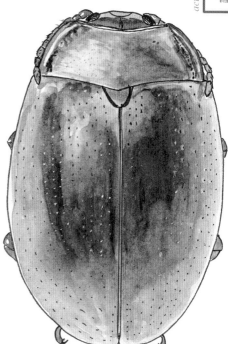

A

B

C

## Chrysolina banksi

There are 16 species of *Chrysolina* beetles recorded from various habitats, but no information available with reference to *C. banksi*.

The larvae of *Chrysolina* beetles feed during the Spring and Summer on the leaves of various plants, making a typical pattern of holes as they do so. Many of them are restricted to a single plant species. Adults appear late in the year and overwinter.

*Body length 10 - 11mm*

**A:** the epipleura, or flange which can be seen outside the body on the underside
**B:** the hind part of the thorax
**C:** the first segment of the abdomen

# Superfamily Curculionoidea

The head is more or less elongated, prolonged into a beak or rostrum. The antennae are elbowed and clubbed, the first segment (the scape) is retractable into a groove in the rostrum. Some eight families in Europe, all those dealt with here in the Family Curculionidae, the weevils.

## Weevils - Family Curculionoidae

Antennae clubbed and elbowed. Rostrum at least as long as wide. Thorax never with side borders, the wing cases (elytra) at front clearly broader than the thorax. Body often covered with small scales. Tarsal formula ( number of segments in fore, mid and hind feet) 4 : 4 : 4. Some segments of the tarsi lobed.
The family is divided into two series: Adelognatha (the Entiminae of some authors) and Phanerognatha.

## Broad-nosed Weevils - Series Adelognatha

The rostrum is short and broad, usually not more than one and a half times as long as wide.

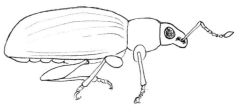

## Long-nosed Weevils - Series Phanerognatha

The rostrum is normally long and narrow, usually very much longer than one and a half times its width.

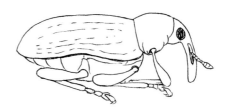

# Beech Leaf-Mining Weevil

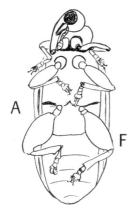

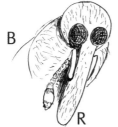

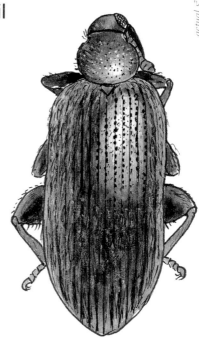

*Rhynchaenus fagi*

This weevil is common wherever there are the beech trees on which it lives. The adult beetles feed on the leaves, leaf stalks and flowers. They lay their eggs on the young leaf veins in Spring and the larvae which hatch from these eggs dig into the leaf and feed on it, making a blotch-shaped mine as they do so. They may be present in such numbers and destroy so many leaves that the growth of the tree and its production of beech nuts is reduced. The larvae pupate and the next generation of adults is formed late in the year. These drop down into the leaf litter on the ground and overwinter in this protected place.

The beetles have a scraper on the upper surface of the abdomen, and a file, made of a series of little pegs on the tips of the wing cases. They can use these to make chirping sounds by scraping one over the other, The males use these sounds in courtship, when females who are interested remain silent, but those who do not care for that particular male make return chirping sounds.

*Body length 3 - 3.5mm*

**A:** underside of beetle
   F: femur of hind leg
**B:** head from the front
   R  rostrum or beak

# Cabbage Stem Weevil

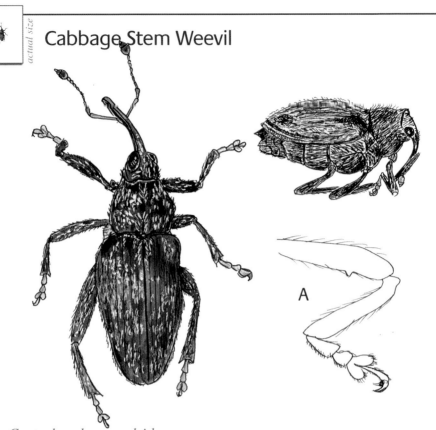

A

*Ceutorhynchus quadridens*

Compared with the broad-nosed spider weevil and shining bud weevil this is a long-nosed weevil, the nose or rostrum being many times longer than wide.

It is quite common on all sorts of brassicas - cabbages, cauliflowers, rape etc. ( the specimen illustrated was captured on broccoli). The adult weevil lays her eggs on the stems in May and June and these hatch in 1 - 4 weeks. The larvae eat out the insides of the leaf stalks, leaf ribs and stems so that damage is internal and not visible, but the plants wilt and young plants will die. A large scale infestation with the weevil can cause serious crop losses.

The larvae are fully grown in 3-6weeks, at which time they leave the plant and enter the soil, where they make a cocoon of soil particles cemented together with their sticky spittle. The adults emerge in mid April and browse on leaves and seeds. A second generation appears in July and August and these adult beetles later overwinter in the shelter of the field margins.

*Body length 2.5 - 3.5mm*

**A:** hind leg showing the tooth on the femur which is characteristic of this weevil

# Clover Weevil

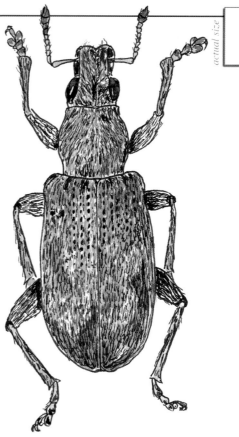

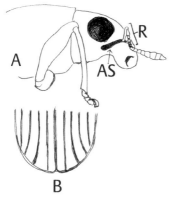

*Sitona lepidus*

The clover weevil is a broad-nosed weevil which is widespread and common in grasslands, agricultural fields and wastelands on all types of soil. It is found on clovers, especially red clover and white clover where it sometimes becomes a minor pest. The female weevil lays her eggs in late Summer and the larvae which emerge feed on the clover leaves. They are fully grown by the time Winter comes and they overwinter as larvae. Adult weevils can also overwinter and lay their eggs the following Spring so that a succession of newly emerged adult beetles can be produced from May onwards.

The clover weevil has been introduced into North America, where it is not a native, and there it has become a pest of lucerne crops.

*Body length 4 - 6mm*

**A:** side view of head and upper thorax
  **R:** rostrum or beak
  **AS:** antennal scrobe, i.e. the furrow into which the antenna fits when it is folded down
**B:** lower part of wing cases to show arrangement of stripes

# Dock Weevil

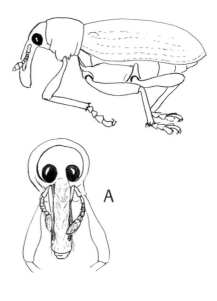

A

*Hypera rumicis*

A common and widespread weevil in the British Isles, in open places, roadsides, field margins and coastal areas, wherever its major food plants, docks, are found.

The weevil lays its eggs on the leaves, making dark, blister-like spots, and the larvae hatch from these to feed on the dock leaves.

The larvae are legless, but are well able to move about by crawling, assisted by the little suction pads on the underside of the body. The larvae finally pupate within a transparent, net-like cocoon which they spin and attach to the stem or leaf of the plant.

Dock plants are a minor pest of agriculture as they reduce the yield of crops in which they grow, and are also unpalatable to grazing animals. They are difficult and expensive to control, they are hard to pull up and they produce long-lived seeds which can germinate up to 20 years later. For these reasons, biological control, using insects such as the dock weevil, is under consideration.

*Body length 4 - 5mm*
**A:** head from front

# Shining Bud Weevil

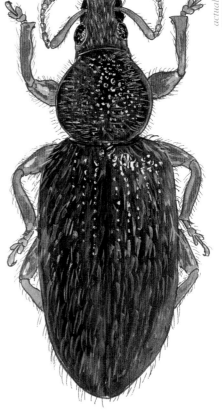

A

*Barypeithes pellucidus*

Despite the 'shining' name this is a rather hairy beetle. It is another of the broad-nosed weevils, with the nose not much longer than wide.

The wing-cases are fused so that it cannot fly. It is thus ground-living, but also can climb into the bushes of hedgerows where it is often found, it also occurs in open grassy places and wood margins.

The shining bud weevil is both common and widespread in the British Isles. It is nocturnal in habit. It has a wide variety of food and, like its relative, the Spider weevil, it also feeds on raspberries to the extent of being a minor pest.

*Body length 2 - 4mm*

**A:** side view of head

*actual size*

# Spider Weevil, Strawberry Fruit Weevil

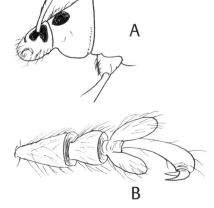

A

B

*Barypeithes araneiformis*

A common and widespread weevil, found in grassy places and infrequently in hedgerows. It differs from most other weevils in that it is shiny and lacks any hairs or scales on the wing-cases and thorax. It is one of the broad-nosed weevils, its nose (or rostrum) is not much longer than it is wide. The wing-cases are fused together so the beetle is unable to fly.

The beetle hides by day under leaves and moss, when night comes it emerges and climbs up on to various plants to feed. It is very fond of strawberries and raspberries as well as other soft fruit and young trees. It bores into the fruit and thus spoils it, to the extent of becoming a pest in gardens and orchards.

*Body length 3 - 4mm*

**A:** lateral view of head
**B:** view of foot of the middle leg from the underside

# Vine Weevil

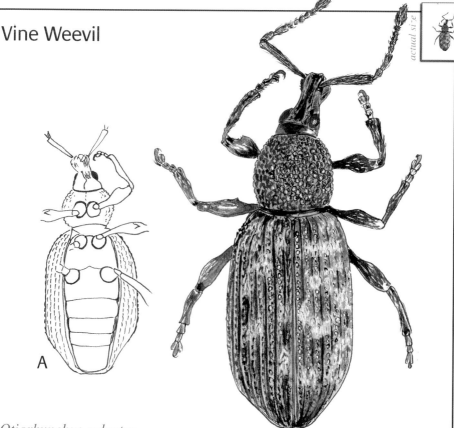

*actual size*

A

## Otiorhynchus sulcatus

This broad-nosed weevil is common and widespread in the British Isles in flat country, where it feeds on a wide range of plants.

Only females, which can reproduce without males, are known from most of the area it inhabits; Italy is the only country where both sexes are recorded. The beetle is active from Spring to Autumn, hiding by day and feeding by night. Both the adult beetle and the larvae are frequently a pest to both agriculturists and horticulturists. The beetle eats notches in the leaves and sometimes ring-barks young plants, and the larvae damage the roots. The female lays her eggs, up to 800, in the

soil in July. These hatch after 1-2 weeks and the larvae move to the nearby root systems on which they feed, causing the affected plants to suddenly wilt and die. They persist for many months, overwintering until the following Spring, when they pupate, each in a small earthen cell.

They are found not only outdoors in gardens but also indoors and in greenhouses where their attack can do much damage to the plants.

*Body length 8 - 10mm*

**A:** underside of beetle

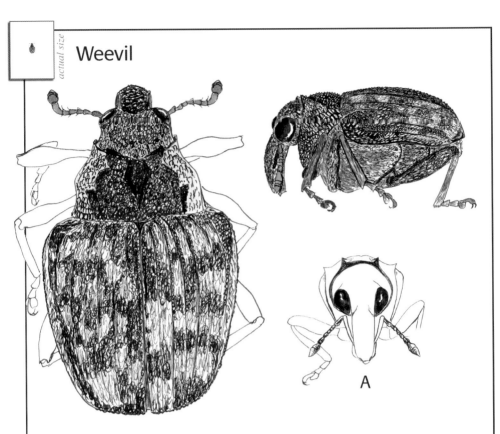

*actual size*

# Weevil

A

## Pelenomus quadrituberculatus

This fascinating little weevil has no distinctive common name, and it is very difficult to find much information about it. This is a common situation for an insect which is neither large and colourful, nor an annoying pest.

*Pelenomus* is found in damp pasture-lands, and has various food-plants, the main ones being the knotweeds. The larvae eat the leaves and flowers and spin themselves a cocoon in which to pupate, either within the food-plant or in the soil.

*Body length 3mm*
**A:** head from the front

# Bugs - Order Hemiptera

Bugs all feed on liquids, and have mouthparts adapted to this method of feeding, i.e. needle-like and hollow, for piercing and sucking. The mouthparts are referred to as a rostrum, or sometimes a beak, and this is held under the head when not in use, pointing downwards or backwards, but never forwards. Most mature bugs have two pairs of wings. The order is divided into three sub-orders - Sternorrhyncha, Auchenorrhyncha and Heteroptera; Sternorrhyncha and Auchenorrhyncha being subdivisions of the former Homoptera.

## Sub-order Sternorrhyncha

Includes the aphids, white flies and scale insects. Wings, when present, are uniform, membranous and held roof-like at rest. The rostrum (R) arises from below the head but forward of the front pair of legs. The antennae (A) consist of four to six elongate segments (see diagram below). Aphids bear on the rear of the abdomen two obvious siphunculi (S) (or cornicles) and a terminal cauda, (C).

## Sub-order Auchenorrhyncha

Includes plant hoppers, cicadas and spittle bugs. The wings are uniform in texture and membranous (see below: A), and at rest are held roof-like over the abdomen. The head is extended backwards so that the rostrum arises between the front pair of legs (see below: B). The antennae characteristically consist of a few short segments with a long terminal bristle.

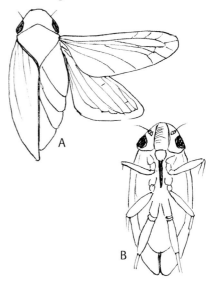

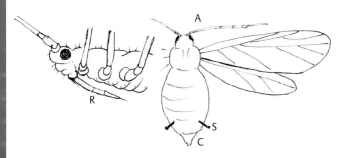

# Bugs - Order Hemiptera

## Sub-order Heteroptera

Includes the true water bugs and land bugs with forewings divided into two distinct regions, a leathery basal portion and a membranous tip. When folded the wings lie flat and the membranous wingtips overlap. The rostrum arises from the front of the head.

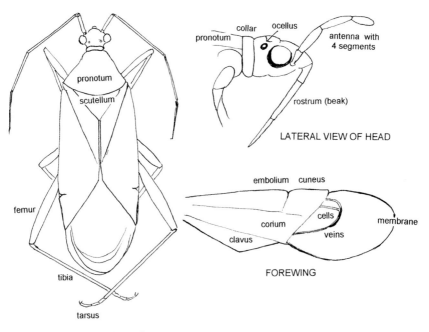

LATERAL VIEW OF HEAD

FOREWING

DORSAL VIEW OF BUG

# Bugs - Order Hemiptera

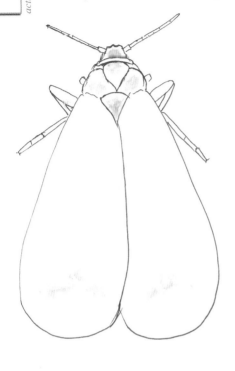

# Honeysuckle Whitefly

*actual size*

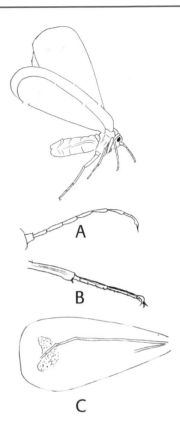

A

B

C

*Aleyrodes lonicerae*

The honeysuckle whitefly looks like a tiny moth, but is in fact, a sap-sucking bug. It is common and widespread, feeding on the leaves of a wide variety of plants.

When a branch heavily infested by the whitefly is disturbed, particularly in dry weather, they fly up in a cloud before settling once again. Underneath the leaves are patches of white, powdery wax and the honeydew which is excreted by both adult whiteflies and their larvae.

Eggs are laid in Spring on the undersides of the leaves, hatching in 1-2 weeks to flat scale-like larvae generally referred to as nymphs. These are fully grown in about 10 days and they then pupate.

Pupation is brief and a new generation of adults appears in a few days. There are usually four generations per year and the adults (mated females) overwinter.

Note: First juvenile stages are called larvae when they appear different from the adult eg. the caterpillar (larva) of the butterfly. They are called nymphs when the larva is similar to the adult, as in many of the bugs.

*Body length 1.4 - 1.6mm*

A: detail of antenna
B  detail of tarsal section of leg
C: forewing to show venation

# Aphids Superfamily Aphidoidea

Wings, when present, membranous.
Antennae (A) with 1-6 segments.
Siphunculae (S) and cauda (C) present.
Tarsi 2-segmented, with a pair of
claws.

## Family Aphididae

It is characteristic of this family that
members of the Spring and Summer
colonies do not lay eggs but produce
active young, asexually.(see over)

### Subfamily Aphidinae

Aphids usually with long antennae (A),
the sixth (terminal) segment with a
process which is longer than the
slightly swollen base. Paired tubes
which are at least half as long as wide,
usually much longer, arise on the back
on the rear of the abdomen, the
siphunculae (S) or cornicles. When
alarmed, many species can exude
drops of liquid containing an alarm
pheromone from the siphunculae.
The body never has a coating of long
hairs.

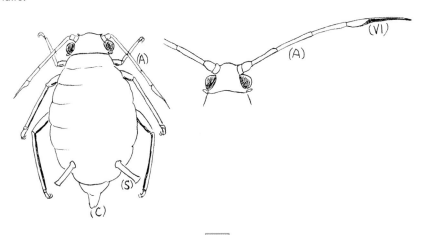

# Life cycle of the black bean aphid
## *Aphis fabae*

Eggs (A) are laid in late Autumn on the stems of the primary host which is the spindle tree (*Euonymus europaeus*). These eggs overwinter.  In Spring, as the spindle tree comes into leaf, these eggs hatch into wingless female aphids (B) which reproduce asexually to produce colonies of active young which feed on the spindle tree. In April, winged females (C) are produced. These seek out the secondary host, the broad bean (*Vicia faba*) and reproduce rapidly to form extensive colonies of wingless forms (D).

When the colony becomes overcrowded, winged forms (E) appear and fly away to colonise new bean plants. This cycle continues throughout the Summer.

In Autumn, winged male (G) and female (F) aphids are produced and these fly to the primary host, the spindle tree.The winged females produce a sexually active female (H) which, after mating with the male, lays her eggs to start the cycle for the following year.

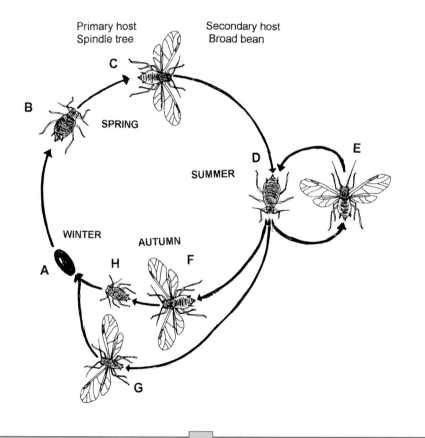

BUGS

# Black Bean Aphid

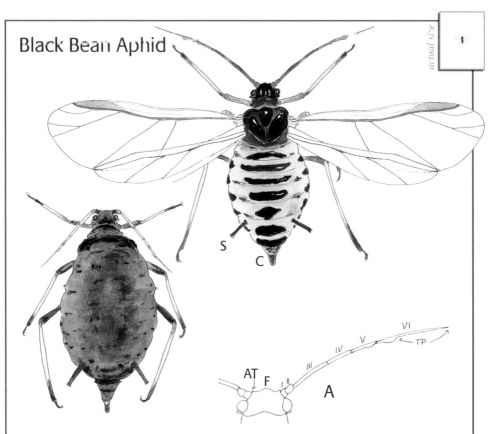

S
C

AT F A

I II III IV V VI TP

*Aphis fabae*

This common and widespread aphid is a major pest of broad beans, other vegetable crops, ornamental plants and weed plants such as thistles, docks and goosefoot. It is, however, the only aphid which is found on the broad bean itself. As with many other aphid species the broad bean aphid has an alternation of generations as shown in the diagram on the preceding page.

The aphids not only reduce yield from the bean plant by feeding on it , but they also produce quantities of sweet honeydew on which the fungus sooty mould will grow. A further disadvantage is that the aphid can be a carrier of plant disease viruses.

These aphids are often also tended by ants which do this for the reward of the honeydew which they enjoy eating. The ants guard the aphids and if a predator such as a ladybird appears the ants will either pick it up (if it is a larva) and drop it over the side of the leaf or, if it is an adult beetle, attack it and drive it away

*Body length 2mm*

Upper illustration winged aphid
Lower illustration wingless aphid
    S:   siphunculus
    C:   cauda
**A:**  Head and antenna
    I, II, III ...VI: segments of the antenna
    TP: terminal process of antenna
    F:   frons or forehead
    AT: small tubercles at the bases of the antennae

# Mealy Aphid, Mealy Cabbage Aphid

*actual size*

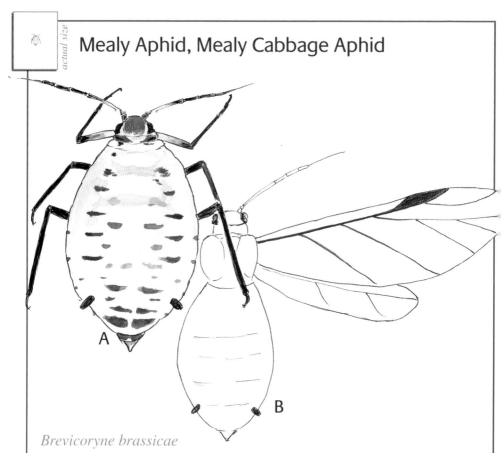

A

B

*Brevicoryne brassicae*

This aphid, which is widespread and common on plants of the cabbage family (cabbage, cauliflower, broccoli, Brussels sprouts as well as kale, rape, radish, swedes and mustard). Unlike the black bean aphid, the cabbage aphid has only a single host plant. Infestation by the aphid is easily recognised by the thick coating of whitish waxy powder which it produces.

It is a pest because the leaves on which it feeds become twisted and distorted. It has the further disadvantage in that it can carry and transmit viruses that cause diseases such as cauliflower mosaic and broccoli necrotic yellows. The aphid lays its eggs in October on stems and leaves.

These eggs overwinter and hatch in the following Spring to give females. These newly hatched young aphids feed on the host plant and reproduce rapidly. From May to July winged forms are produced and these fly away to find new plants to feed on, and thus the aphid infestation can spread through the whole vegetable crop. In mild winters the adults may survive through to the following Spring, and presumably this will become more common with global warming.

*Body length 2 - 3mm*

**A:** wingless form
**B:** winged form

70

BUGS

# Campion Aphid

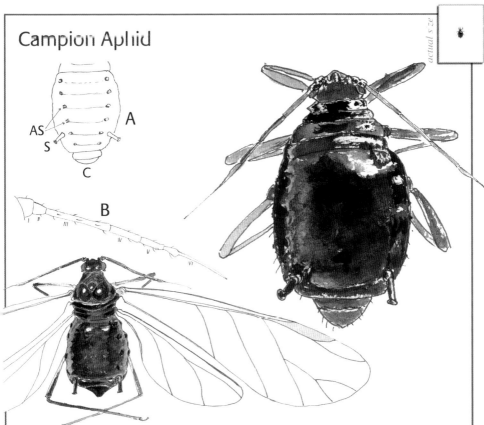

*Brachycaudus klugkisti*

Widespread in Europe on the food plants which are species of campion. This aphid is very obvious when a dense infestation occurs because the numerous black aphids crowded together on the upper stems of the campion plant make it quite conspicuous.

This is not be the only aphid that lives on the campion plant. A closely related species, *(Brachycaudus lychnidis)* is also common, and it is not easy to tell them apart as they differ only in slight anatomical details. The aphids illustrated were collected from red campion growing in the garden.

*Body length 2 - 3mm*

Upper illustration wingless aphid
Lower illustration winged aphid
**A:** dorsal surface of the abdomen of the wingless aphid
    S:   siphunculus
    C:   cauda
    AS:  abdominal spiracles
**B:** antenna with 6 segments

# Knapweed Aphid

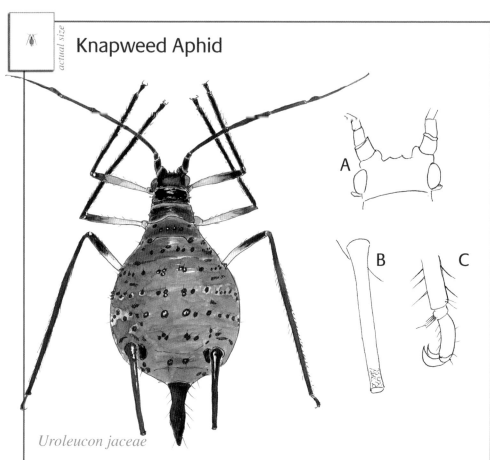

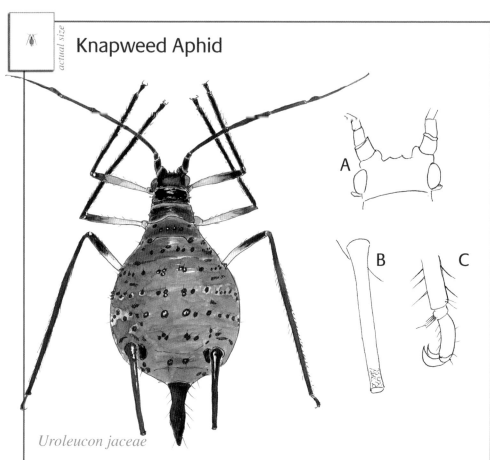

*Uroleucon jaceae*

A
B
C

This rather large, shining brownish-black aphid was collected in August on plants of black knapweed growing by the roadside. The aphids were forming quite a large colony on the plant. In having only one host plant species it resembles many other *Uroleucon* species, each of which is typically found on only one species of composite, such as thistle, chicory, yarrow, coltsfoot or dandelion.

It is another example of an aphid that infests a non-commercial host plant, so that little study has been done on it, and thus little information is available. By contrast, serious pests of economic crops, such as the black bean aphid, have been intensively studied so that much information is available about them.

*Body length 3 - 4mm*

**A:** aphid head
**B:** siphunculus
**C:** foot (end of tarsus) with claw

# Mint Aphld

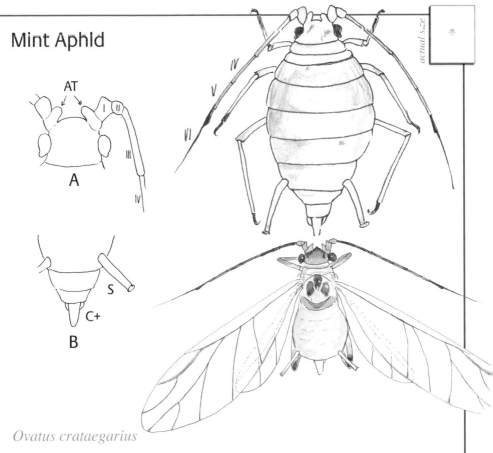

*Ovatus crataegarius*

This little green aphid has two host plants. In Spring they form small colonies on the shoot tips of the hawthorn bush, and here they appear to do little damage.

In Summer, colonies are formed on both wild and garden mint plants and here they are a pest, making the mint almost useless as a foodstuff. (No mint sauce for your roast Manx lamb!)

The mint aphid's life cycle is influenced by the weather. If the weather during the year is mild, only females which reproduce asexually are present throughout the entire year. When the Winters are severe the aphids overwinter as eggs on the hawthorn.

*Body length 2mm*

**A:** aphid head
AT: antennal tubercles
I,II,III,...VI: segments of the antenna
**B:** hind end of the aphid, dorsal surface
S: siphunculus
C+: cauda

# Common Frog Hopper

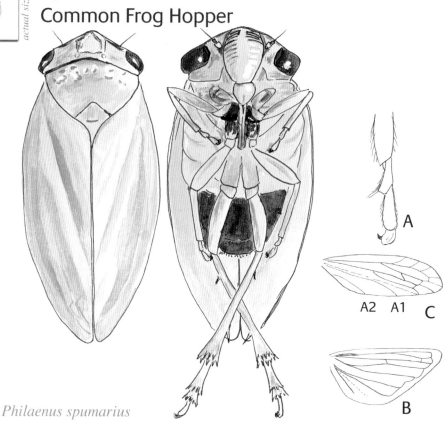

*Philaenus spumarius*

A

A2   A1   C

B

Very widespread and common, found in any place where plants, both woody or herbaceous, are growing.

Adult frog hoppers are in evidence from June to September or October, feeding on many different plants by sucking the plant sap. One curious feature is that they show twelve different colour patterns, which to first sight gives the appearance that they are different species. The differences are genetically determined, but there is also some evidence that the dark forms occur in areas where there is air pollution.

Adults lay eggs in late September and these eggs overwinter, hatching in the following Spring. The larvae, or nymphs as they are called, feed on the host plant, each one surrounding itself with a white froth known as "cuckoo spit" so the nymph is commonly called a "spittle bug". These nymphs are a minor pest of cultivated plants, particularly fruit crops such as raspberries and strawberries, ornamental plants, and crop plants such as sugar beet.

*Body length 6mm*

**A:** foreleg, last segments of tarsus and claw
**B:** forewing, A1 , A2 ,anal veins
**C:** hindwing

# Sage Hopper, Chrysanthemum Hopper

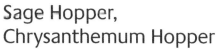

A

— V
→ P
← S

B
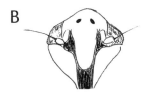

C

D

*Euptery melissae*

Widespread and common in the British Isles, found on a number of cultivated ornamental plants including chrysanthemums and also herbs such as sage, mint and others of the same family.

The sage hopper is an insect with well developed hind legs which enables it to jump very actively. The hoppers feed on the upper surface of the leaves of the host plant which are thus distorted and damaged. Information on its life history is sparse, but it is known that related species of *Eupteryx* have two generations per year and overwinter as eggs.

Body length 3 - 4mm

A: dorsal view of head and pronotum
  V: vertex
  P: pronotum
  S: scutellum
B: ventral view of head
C: forewing
D: hindwing

# Capsid Bugs - Family Miridae

A large family of very common bugs, comprising over 30% of the sub-order Heteroptera. With some 750 genera and up to 8000 species.

The insects are generally delicate and soft-bodied, 2-11mm long. The family includes both plant-feeders and predators. There is one generation per year and the usual over-wintering form is the egg.

## Head

Antennae of four segments, always clearly visible from above. Rostrum with four segments, arising from the front of the head and not markedly curved. Ocelli absent.

## Wings

When wings are present the forewing is divided into a tougher basal section which has a cuneus separated by a fold running from the costal fracture; and a clear, membranous wing tip with a semi-circular, usually two-part cell.

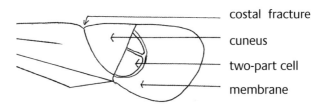

costal fracture

cuneus

two-part cell

membrane

# Capsid Bugs - Family Miridae

## Legs

The second joint of the legs, the trochanter, is apparently two-segmented. Legs can be shed at will, breaking between the two sections of the trochanter. The tarsi are three-segmented. Capsid bugs are very adept at running on leaves due to adhesive pad-like structures developed on the tips of the final tarsal segment. The structure between the claws is called the *arolium* (*pl. arolia*) the one under the claw is called the *pseudoarolium* (*pl. pseudoarolia*).

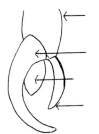

the tarsal segment

claw

pseudoarolia

arolia

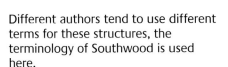

Different authors tend to use different terms for these structures, the terminology of Southwood is used here.

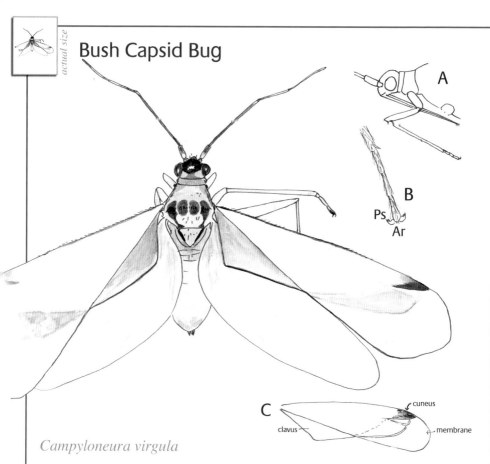

# Bush Capsid Bug

*actual size*

**A:** lateral view of head and pronotum

**B**
Ps
Ar

**C**
cuneus
clavus
membrane

*Campyloneura virgula*

This capsid bug is found throughout the British Isles on a wide variety of shrubs and trees, in particular hawthorn, hazel and oak.

The bugs overwinter as eggs which hatch in May, and the larvae develop into adult bugs in July. Both larvae and adults are quite colourful, the larvae being yellow with red wing cases. Males are very rare and so that this bug must usually reproduce asexually. Adults are active until October, when they lay their eggs which will pass the Winter in a dormant state.

Both the larvae and the adult bugs are predators. Their food includes red spider mites, greenflies and bark lice; also occasionally feeding on the honeydew which they find on leaves.

*Body length 3 - 4mm*

A: lateral view of head and pronotum
B: tarsus and claws
    Ar:   arolia
    Ps    pseudoarolia
C: forewing showing cuneus, membrane and clavus

# Capsid Bug

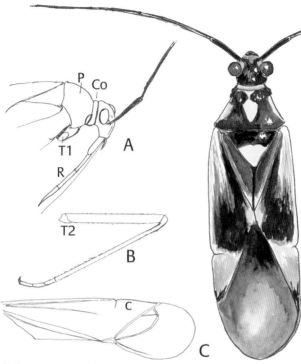

*actual size*

P  Co

T1

R

A

T2

B

c

C

C

*Calocoris stysi*

Widespread and common throughout
Europe in woodland, scrubland,
grassland and along roadsides.
Adult bugs are active from May to
August, laying their eggs in cracks and
crevices in the bark of trees.

The larvae which develop from these
eggs feed on a variety of plants, but
especially on the flowers and young
fruits of the stinging nettle.

They also feed on aphids and other
similar small insects if they have the
opportunity. The adult bugs are often
found on the broad flower heads of
umbelliferous plants such as hogweed.

*Body length 6mm*

A:  lateral view of head and pronotum
    P:  pronotum
    Co: collar
    T1: trochanter of foreleg
    R:  rostrum or beak
B:  hindleg
    T2: trochanter
C:  forewing
    c:  cuneus

BUGS

# Common Green Capsid

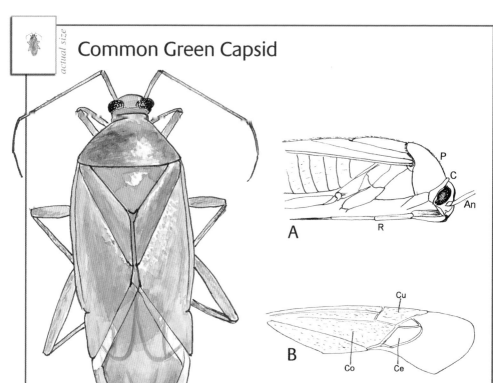

*actual size*

A

P: pronotum
C: collar
An: antenna
R: rostrum

B

Cu

Co

Ce

*Lygocoris pabulinus*

Common and very widespread in habitats of all kinds, including gardens and orchards, where it can reach pest status. The list of host plants is a long one and includes vegetable crops such as beet, beans, potatoes and swedes; also fruit crops such as apples, pears, gooseberries, raspberries and strawberries; and ornamentals such as roses.

Eggs are laid in Autumn, and these eggs overwinter, to hatch in April of the following year. The larvae (nymphs) feed on the leaves of the woody plants on which they were hatched, but when they become adult, they move to feed on herbaceous plants. In late Summer

they lay eggs on these plants and the next generation of adults appears in the Autumn. These adults migrate to the woody plants on which they lay their eggs, and these are the eggs which will overwinter.

*Body length 5 - 7mm*

A: lateral view
   P: pronotum
   C: collar
   An: antenna
   R: rostrum
B: forewing
   Co: corium
   Cu: cuneus
   Ce: cell of the wing membrane

# Common Nettle Capsid

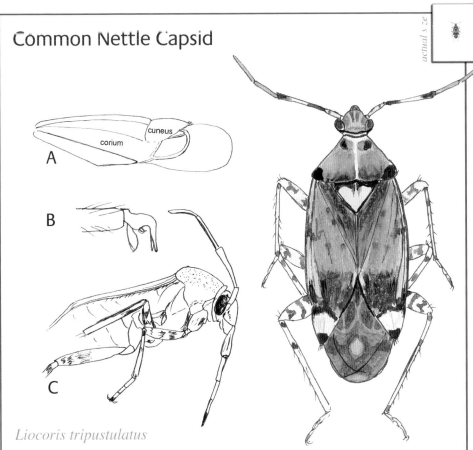

A: forewing — cuneus, corium

B

C

*Liocoris tripustulatus*

A very common capsid, restricted to a single host plant, the stinging nettle, where both larvae and adults feed on the buds, flowers, seeds and leaves. Eggs are laid in June and July, and the adults appear in July and August, these adults will feed during the late Summer and Autumn and hibernate over the Winter.

They will emerge in the following Spring, and lay the eggs which will give rise to the new generation. This capsid has a seasonal variation of colour pattern, the young adults of early Summer are light brown and yellow whilst the overwintering adults are a darker brown.

The insect illustrated was captured in September.

*Body length  4 - 5mm*

A: forewing showing cuneus and corium
B: tip of tarsus and claw
C: side view of insect

*actual size*

# Smooth Capsid Bug

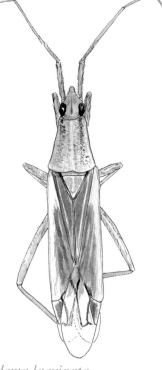

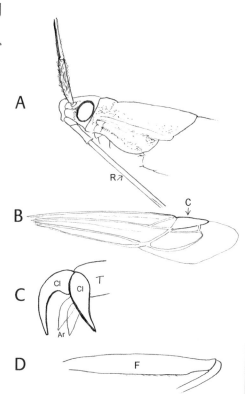

A

B

C

D

*Stenodema laevigata*

Common in grasslands over much of Europe, where it feeds on herbaceous plants. There is one generation each year, and the adults show a varied range of colour forms. Young adults first appear in July and August and these are pale yellow with a reddish-brown pattern of markings.

The markings later fade and the whole insect appears brownish. In late Summer, females are yellow and become brown in the Autumn before they hibernate over the winter.

When they emerge in the following Spring, their colour changes to green. The specific adjective *laevigata* is

given in the neuter form *laevigatum* in some texts.

*Body length 6mm*

**A:** lateral view of head to show rostrum (R)
**B:** forewing to show cuneus (C)
**C:** tip of tarsus
    Cl: claw
    Ar: arolia
**D:** leg
    F: femur

# Common Flower Bug

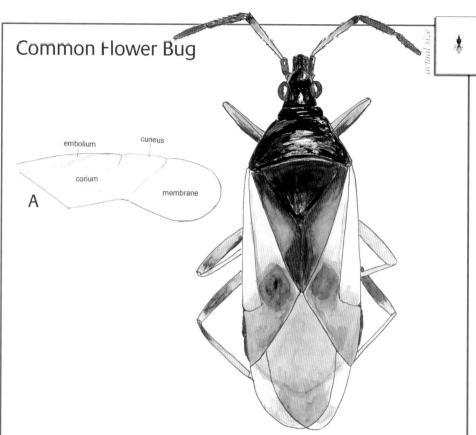

A: embolium, cuneus, corium, membrane

*Anthocoris nemorum*

This is the most abundant and widespread of the British flower bugs, and it also one of the commonest of all bugs.

Adult bugs overwinter under leaf litter or in bark cracks. In March they come out of hibernation and move onto a variety of plants, including willow trees. They are predators and feed on aphids and other small insects. If handled carelessly, they can cause some pain by their ability to pierce the skin and draw blood.

These adults are mostly females which have been fertilised during the previous Autumn before hibernation, but in some years numerous males are also produced. Eggs are laid on the leaves and hatch after a few weeks. The larvae so produced develop into the Summer generation of adults which will commence egg-laying in July. The larvae hatching from these eggs will give rise to the second generation of adults in September. Normally these adults will overwinter, but in years when warm and dry conditions prevail a third generation may be produced.

*Body length 3 - 4mm*

**A:** forewing to show embolium, cuneus, corium and membrane

# Flower Bug

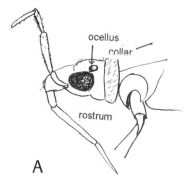

ocellus
collar
rostrum

**A**

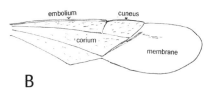

embolium    cuneus
corium
membrane

**B**

*Anthocoris butleri*

The distribution of this bug is not fully known, but it appears to be more common in southern England.

The adults overwinter and come out of hibernation to lay eggs in May and early June on the leaves of the box plant. There are two generations per year, adults of the first generation appearing in July, and of the second generation, which will overwinter, appearing in late August or September.

*Body length 4mm*

**A:** lateral view of head to show collar, ocellus and rostrum

**B:** forewing to show embolium, cuneus, corium and membrane

# Shield Bugs - Family Pentatomidae

Shield bugs are so-called because the adults have scutellum with a shield-like shape. This common name is given to five families within the superfamily Pentatomoidea, the family Pentatomidae being the largest with 17 species in the British Isles.

## Family characteristics

Family characteristics: Mostly oval bugs about 1.5 times or more as long as wide, and more than 3mm long. Head length not more than twice its width. Antennae with 5 segments. Scutellum (S) large and triangular, but not as long as the wings and not reaching to the end of the abdomen.

Abdomen on the underside (I and II) without any obvious, long forward-pointing spine reaching almost to the base of the forelegs, or with a shorter one not reaching beyond the bases of the middle legs. Tibia (Ti) without rows of spines, with only a single spine on the foreleg. Tarsi (Ta) with 3 segments.

I:      lateral view head, thorax and upper abdomen
II:     underside
P:      pronotum
S:      scutellum
Ti:     tibia
Ta:     tarsus
R:      rostrum
FW:     forewing showing the hardened base and the membranous tip

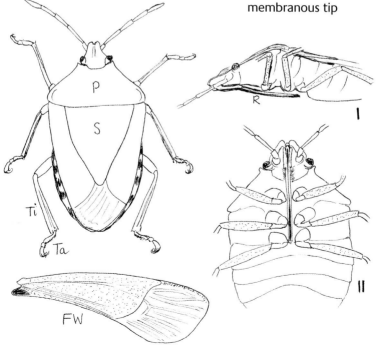

# Forest Bug

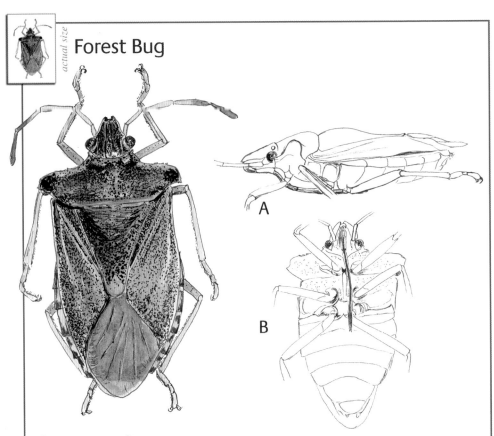

*actual size*

A

B

*Pentatoma rufipes*

This common bug occurs over most of Europe on a wide range of trees and shrubs, often in orchards and gardens. Oak is its preferred host but it may also be found on alder, hazel, apple, pear and cherry.

It is omnivorous, feeding on the sap from leaves, buds and fruit, and also attacking small insects. Eggs are laid in August on the leaves, and these hatch after a few weeks.

The larvae feed for some time before going into hibernation over the winter, when they often form food for foraging coal tits.

The larvae emerge from hibernation in April and develop into adults in July. Mating occurs in July and August, after which the eggs are laid. The males die early, but females often live on until November

*Body length 12 - 15mm*

**A:** lateral view of bug
**B:** ventral view of bug

# Gorse Shieldbug

*actual size*

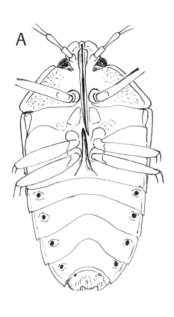

A

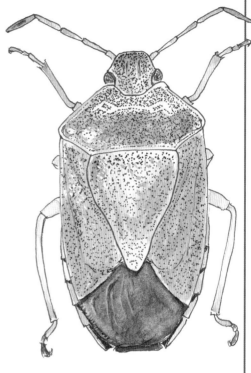

*Piezodorus lituratus*

Common and widely distributed through the British Isles, wherever its food plant, gorse, grows.

Mating activity begins in May, with a complex courtship ritual which includes male song. Eggs are laid on gorse and the larvae from their hatching wander over the gorse plants to find pods with ripe seed, on which they feed. Adults appear in July and these are handsomely coloured in pink and green, a colour scheme which indicates that they are sexually immature. There is only one generation each year, and these immature adults will hibernate on the ground under the gorse bushes,

becoming a brown colour at this stage. They reappear in the following Spring, now bright green, and sexually mature.

Both larvae and adults feed on the ripe seeds of the gorse, but when the gorse pods mature and shoot the seeds out, the shieldbugs have no more interest in the gorse and move off to feed on other legume shrubs and herbs.

*Body length 11 - 12mm*

**A:** ventral surface of bug showing the forward-pointing process between the hind legs, and the black gland openings on the sides of the abdominal segments.

# Sloe Bug, Hairy Shieldbug

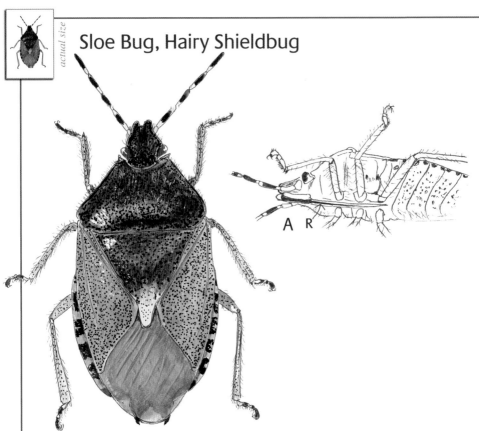

A R

*Dolycoris baccarum*

Resident, common and widely distributed, mainly in the southern parts of the British Isles, in gardens, fields, woodland margins, roadsides and hedges.

There is one generation each year. Adults which have overwintered will mate in June, with a complex mating routine. Eggs are laid on the surface of leaves of the sloe, and other plants of the rose family. The larvae which hatch from these eggs are hairy and feed on the sloe plant, from which fact arise the common names.

Adults appear in August and feed on flowers and fruit of a wide variety of

plants, and also on aphids and beetle eggs before they hibernate for the Winter. The plants which they feed on in late Summer and Autumn include wheat, where the saliva of the bug causes damage so that the baking quality of the flour produced from the affected wheat is reduced.

*Body length 11 - 12mm*

**A:** lateral/ventral view of head and pronotum to show position of rostrum (R)

# Hawthorn Shieldbug

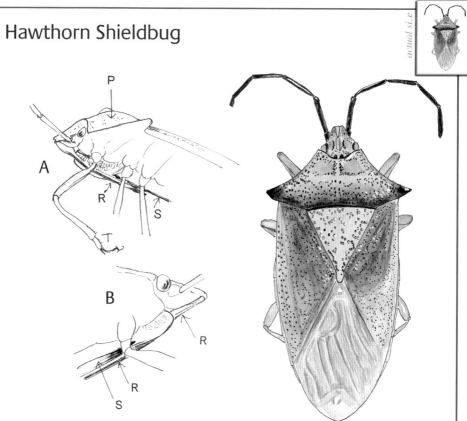

*Acanthosoma haemorrhoidale*

Common over much of Europe, but absent from Scotland, in woodland margins, hedgerows and gardens, wherever hawthorn is growing.

Overwintering adult bugs, which are green to brownish-red in colour, come out of hibernation in April. Eggs are laid from late April until July, so that larvae may be found from early June. Yellowish coloured adults appear in August and September, and these are the ones which will overwinter in cracks in the bark or in tufts of grass. The primary foodstuff is hawthorn berries, but if these are not available the bugs will feed on hawthorn leaves or move to other trees such as oak, whitebeam, rowan, poplar, birch or hazel.

The underside of the abdomen of the adult bug is yellow-green with a red tail-end. It has been suggested that Linnaeus, who named the insect, thought that it looked as if the bug suffered from haemorrhoids ("piles") so gave it the name *"haemorrhoidale"*.

*Body length 13 - 15mm*

**A:** lateral view of head and pronotum (P) from the left side
   **T:** tarsus of foreleg
**B:** lateral view of the head from the right side.
   **R:** rostrum
   **S:** forward-pointing spine

# Butterflies and Moths - Order Lepidoptera

As a rough guide butterflies have knobbed antennae whereas moths have antennae which are not knobbed but are of various shapes, usually threadlike or plumose.

The pattern of veins in the wings is the main character used to separate the families. One problem which arises in consulting various texts is that the veins have been variously named by different authors (See Stresemann). The system invented by Comstock is in fairly general use and will be used here. It is illustrated in the following diagrams.

Veins shown by dotted lines are often weakly developed or absent.

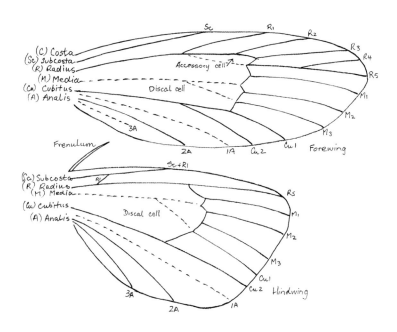

# Butterflies and Moths - Order Lepidoptera

The standard way to see the wing veins is to bleach the wings. This is simply done as follows:

1    Carefully remove the wings from one side of the body.

2    Dip for a few seconds in 95% alcohol (commercial or industrial spirit)

3    Pour off the alcohol and add acid (10%HCl or vinegar)

4    Pour off the acid and add commercial bleach liquid (eg. Clorox) and leave until all colour disappears.

5    Pour off the bleach and rinse the wings well in water. It is then useful to mount them on a glass slide. Have a container large enough to contain the slide and float the wings above it. Carefully bring the slide up under the wings so that they lie on the slide. Check for bubbles and folds and carefully remove them by gently stroking with a soft paint brush. If it is desired to make the mount permanent, allow the wings to dry, place another slide on top and bind the two together. A useful semi-permanent mount may be made by covering the dried wings on the slide with transparent tape. Label the slide.

# Butterflies and Moths - Order Lepidoptera

The arrangement follows the scheme of classification in Maitland Emmet and Heath (1989)

# Golden Pygmy

A

B

*Nepticula aurella*

It is claimed that this is the smallest known moth. Its larva is a common leaf miner of bramble leaves where the curling shape of the mine is typical. The mines can be found in May and June, and in good years a second generation in July and August.

When the larva is fully grown it bites a hole in the mine and moves to the ground, where it pupates among the leaf litter. The adult moths appear in April, July and sometimes in September, but larvae of the last generation stay in the mine and overwinter until the following March.

*Body length 3mm*

**A:** bramble leaf collected in mid-April, the mines are empty as the larvae have left to pupate.
**B:** head of the Golden pygmy from the front, showing the yellow-orange caps over the eyes

# Six-Spot Burnet

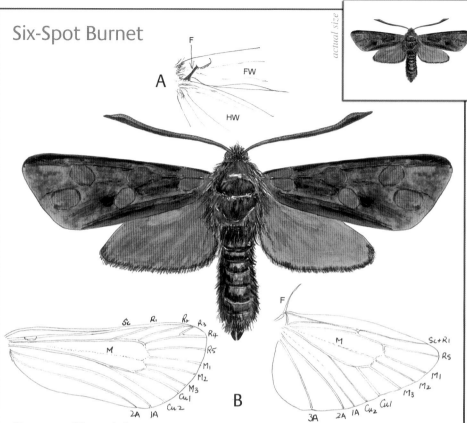

*Zygaena filipendulae*

A common and widespread day-flying moth, conspicuous, brightly coloured and poisonous. The larvae form hydrogen cyanide and the bright colours are warning signs causing birds to avoid eating them.

Burnet moths live in colonies in meadows, woodland and coastal areas, where their food-plants (clovers, trefoils and vetches) commonly grow. Eggs are laid on the food-plant in July and August and the caterpillars which hatch from these eggs feed until late Autumn. They then hibernate until the following Spring when they start feeding again. They are fully grown by the end of May. They pupate in cocoons which are attached to the plant stem, from which the moths emerge in June or July to fly until August or September.

*Body length 15mm*
*Wingspan 33mm*

**A:** underside of the forewing (FW) and hindwing (HW) near the body, to show the frenulum (F) with its tip in the pocket of the forewing
**B:** veins of forewing (upper) and hindwing (lower) with standard enumeration of the veins
  Sc: subcosta
  R: radius
  M: media
  Cu: cubitus
  A: anal

# Common Clothes Moth

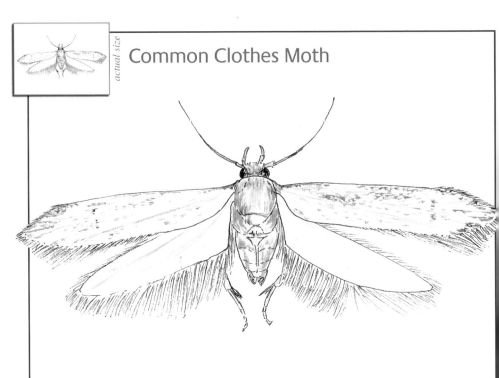

## Tineola biselliella

This little moth is commonly about in early Summer to Autumn. The larvae are serious pests. They eat a wide variety of substances including woollen cloth, clothing, carpets, and many other materials. It is destructive not only in the home but also in places such as museums where it damages animal and bird specimens. It has even been recorded as doing serious damage to the insulation of a London telephone exchange.

The moth has a short life, usually only a week or thereabouts, during which time it will lay up to 200 eggs in places suitable for the larvae to feed (such as your favourite woollen jumper!). All the phases of its life, including the time of egg hatching, depend on temperature. The hatching time varies from 37 days at 12°C to 5 days at 29°C.

If food is adequate and temperature right the larva will grow to full size and spin a cocoon in which it pupates. It may, however, go into a resting phase which can last for years. Usually, however, the pupal phase lasts from 14 - 44 days after which the male and female moths emerge and mate.

*Body length 6mm*
*Wingspan 14mm*

# Suborder Frenatae Family Oecophoridae

## Suborder Frenatae

A frenulum (F) is present on the upper surface of the hindwing, and vein Rs is unbranched in the hindwing.

## Family Oecophoridae

Small, somewhat flattened moths with usually smooth scales on the head. The palps (LP) are long and curving upwards. The antennae are longer than half the forewing length, and the first segment carries a distinct tuft of hairs, the pectin (P).

The wings are rather broad, more or less rounded at the apex, the hindwing almost, or as wide as, the forewing. All 12 veins are present in the forewing. Vein Cu2 arises in the outer part of the discal cell (DC), and veins R4 and R5 are stalked. In the hindwing all 8 veins are present, veins

RS and M1 are separate and run more or less parallel. The hind tibiae are hairy.

There are four subfamilies, of which the two Oecophorinae and Depressariinae contain the majority of species, including those illustrated here. The two subfamilies are separated by the presence of ocelli on the head (Depressariinae) or its absence (Oecophorinae).

There are four subfamilies, of which the two Oecophorinae and Depressariinae contain the majority of species, including those illustrated here. The two subfamilies are separated by the presence or absence of ocelli on the head. They are present in the subfamily Depressariinae and absent from the subfamily Oecophorinae.

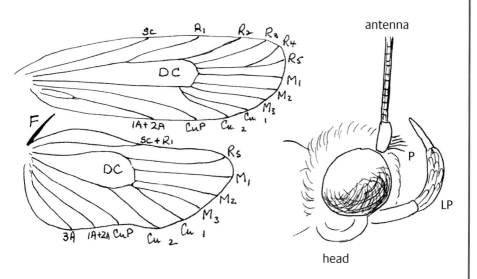

*actual size*

# Brown House Moth

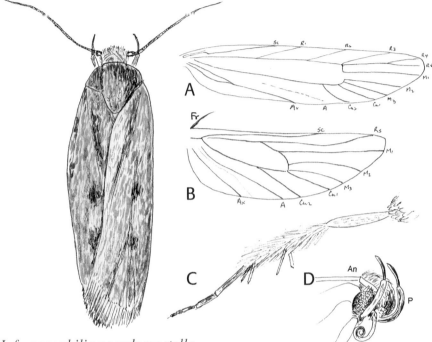

A
B
Fr
C
D
An
P

*Hofmannophilia pseudospretella*

Distributed over almost the whole world, preferring cooler conditions so only in mountainous areas of hot countries.

Very common in houses, outhouses, gardens and bird's nests. Flying from May to September. Eggs are laid in May and June and the larvae hatch after 3-4 weeks. They feed on animal and vegetable refuse, wool, carpets, books, furs, skins, dead insects, seeds, groceries, stored foods and almost any other stored product.

They are not only an obvious household pest, but their fondness for books and museum specimens makes them a

serious pest of museums and libraries. The larvae hibernate over the winter period and pupate at the feeding site in a cocoon made of mixed silk and feeding debris. Adults moths emerge in about 10 days.

*Body length 7mm*
*Wingspan 15 - 25mm*

A: forewing
B: hind wing
   Fr:   frenulum
C: hind leg
D: lateral view of head
   P:   palp
   An:  base of antenna

98

# Little Sulphur Moth

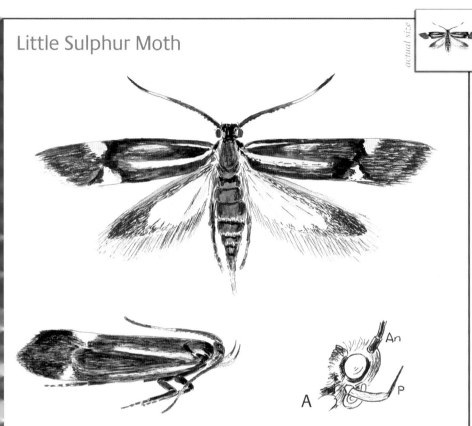

*Esperia sulphurella*

A small but colourful day-flying moth, usually found in open woodland, but sometimes also in gardens in the country.

Adults fly from May to July; the males fly in the mornings, gathering round any females that they can find in order to mate. Eggs are laid during this period, in groups of one to three, end to end in cracks and crevices in dead wood, and sometimes in wooden fence posts and palings.

The larvae hatching from these eggs feed on fungi, particularly the large bracket fungi often found on tree trunks. The larvae are relatively long-

lived, overwintering and pupating in the following late Spring or Summer, in a cocoon which they spin at the feeding site.

*Body length 7mm*
*Wingspan 15 - 25mm*

**A:** side view of head
**P:** palp
**An:** base of antenna

# White-Shouldered House Moth

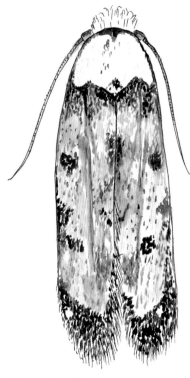

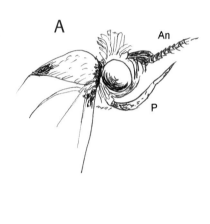

A

An

P

*Endrosis sarcitrella*

A common moth, found almost world-wide. Easily recognised by its white head and shoulders.

The moth flies from April to October, but the larvae may be found all the year, feeding on virtually anything that they can find. It has been known to attack any stored foodstuffs, corn, seed potatoes, grain, seeds such as peas and many others. It has even been recorded as a serious pest in wine cellars where it eats the corks of the bottles.

It is common both in houses and outdoors, and sometimes is found overwintering in haystacks.

*Body length 5mm*
*Forewing length 5 - 9mm*

**A:** side view of head
**P:** palp
**An:** base of antenna

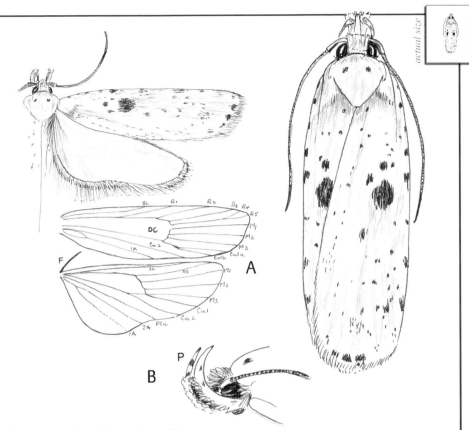

## Agonopterix subpropinquella

Rather common throughout Europe on open ground such as roadside verges, hillsides and waste ground, wherever thistles flourish.

The eggs are laid on thistles and related plants in May. These hatch in 3-4 weeks into a caterpillar larva. The caterpillar eats a mine in the leaf of the food plant and either rolls the leaf into a tube in which it can hide, or spins a web on the underside of the leaf in which it hides and feeds.
In July the full-grown larva finds its way down to the soil where it spins a cocoon and pupates within it.

In August, the moth appears from the

pupa, it hides in dense plant cover and finally overwinters until the following May.

*Body length 9mm*
*Wingspan 14 - 22mm*

**A:** forewing (above) and hindwing (below)
    F: frenulum
    DC: discal cell
    SC: subcostal vein
    R: radial
    M: medial
    Cu: cubital
    A: anal veins
**B:** head from the side
    P: the long, curved palps

# Sycamore Tortrix Moth

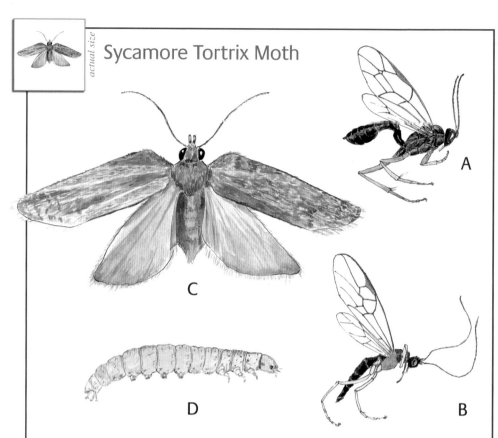

*actual size*

A: Ichneumon wasp
B: Braconid wasp
C: Sycamore tortrix moth
D: caterpillar of Sycamore tortrix moth

## Acleris sparsana

The adult moths fly from August to May, during the evenings. Eggs are laid on leaves of sycamore, and also field maple, beech and hornbeam trees. The larvae hatch out in June and spin themselves a web, rolling up the leaf as they do so, and thus concealing themselves within the rolled-up leaf. They are fully grown by late July or August and at this stage they spin a cocoon in which to pupate, usually in the leaf.

Rolled-up leaves containing moth larvae were collected from a sycamore tree. From these larvae three different insects developed: the Sycamore tortrix moth which is illustrated, and also two wasps which had parasitized other moth larvae. These wasps use the long, sharp ovipositor at the rear end of their body to bore into the caterpillar`s body and deposit their eggs. The wasp larva slowly eats the caterpillar and finally pupates, usually within the old caterpillar skin. Braconid wasps overwinter as larvae within the host caterpillar, but Ichneumon wasps overwinter as adults.

*Body length 6.5mm*
*Wingspan 17mm*

A: Ichneumon wasp *(Tranosema)*, length 5mm
B: Braconid wasp *(Charmon)*, length 5mm
C: Sycamore tortrix moth
D: caterpillar of Sycamore tortrix moth, length 10mm

# Close-Wing Grass Moth

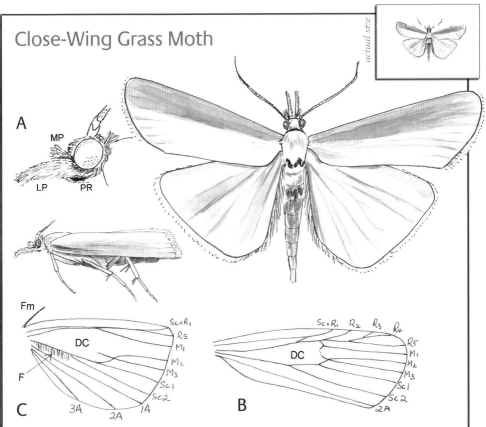

A
MP
LP    PR

Fm
DC
F
C    3A    2A    1A
$Sc+R_1$
$R_5$
$M_1$
$M_2$
$M_3$
$Sc_1$
$Sc_2$

$Sc+R_1$    $R_2$    $R_3$    $R_4$
DC
B
$R_5$
$M_1$
$M_2$
$M_3$
$Sc_1$
$Sc_2$
$2A$

*Chrysoteuchia culmella*

This rather inconspicuous little moth is common and abundant from June to August wherever grass is growing. It flies in the evening and night-time; however, if the grass is disturbed by walking through it in the daytime the males fly up out of the grass, but the females hide in the thick grass bases. When the moth is resting on a grass stem it holds its wings very close to its body, which is the reason for its common name.

The larvae are found on sheep's fescue grass from September to April, feeding until late Autumn. They then migrate down to the soil surface where they spin a protective cocoon in which they overwinter. They pupate in the following May and emerge as adult moths in June.

*Body length 9mm*
*Wingspan 19mm*

A:  Side view of head
    LP:  labial palp
    MP:  maxillary palp
    PR:  proboscis
B:  forewing
C:  hindwing
    DC:  discal cell
    Sc, R, M, & A:  subcostal, radial, medial and anal veins
    Fm:  frenulum
    F:  fringe of hairs

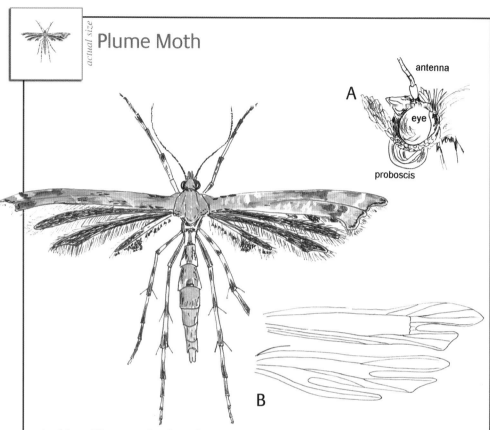

*actual size*

# Plume Moth

A

antenna

eye

proboscis

B

*Amblyptilia acanthodactyla*

A night-flying moth, very common and widespread in open country, hedges, woodland and heathland. It is unusual and easy to recognise because the wings are split lengthwise into a number of sections, each resembling a feather or plume, hence its common name.

In the daytime it hides among the plants, coming out at night to feed. The larvae feed on the buds, flowers and seeds of a number of plants, including mints, heather and geraniums. When the larva is fully grown it pupates and attaches itself between the seed pods where it looks just like a dry flower.

There are two generations each year. The adult moths appear in July and again in September. In November they go into hibernation and overwinter, to fly again the following Spring.

*Body length 6.5mm*
*Wingspan 17mm*

**A:** detail head from the side
**B:** forewing and hindwing

# Plume Moth

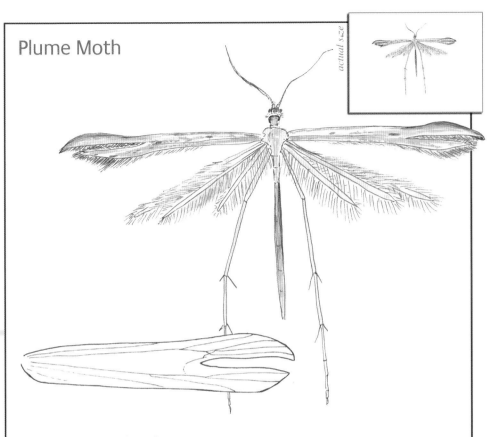

*actual size*

*Emmelina monodactyla*

A common moth of the hedgerows and similar places. In the daytime it rests among the shrubs with its forewings closely rolled around the hindwings and the legs stretched out in line with the body, thus looking rather like a bare twig. At dusk it begins to fly and feeds during the night.

Eggs are laid in May and the larvae feed for preference on the young shoots of the bindweed. When fully grown they pupate on the food plant until July, when the adult moths appear.

In the Autumn the moths look for dry places in thick growths of ivy or bramble clumps where they hibernate until the next Spring.

*Body length 11mm*
*Wingspan 27mm*

**A:** Lower diagram, detail of forewing, the fringe is omitted

BUTTERFLIES

# Whites and Yellows - Family Pieridae

Small to medium sized, usually white, yellow or orange with black markings. Antennae arising near each other, never longer than half the forewing length, antennal club rather small. Ocelli absent. Forewing with radius 3- or 4-branched, hindwing with 2 anal veins (see below). Front legs normal, tarsal claws forked. Often dimorphic, with differences between males and females, and also between early and late season generations.

## Subfamily Pierinae

Humeral vein present in the hindwing. British species mostly white.

*Pieris*

Both sexual and seasonal dimorphism obvious. Antennal club with rounded tip and tapering sharply at the base. Forewing with vein R3 absent, veins R4 and R5 branching from a common stalk. The diagram shows the forewing (upper) and hindwing (lower) of the Small White (*Pieris rapae*).

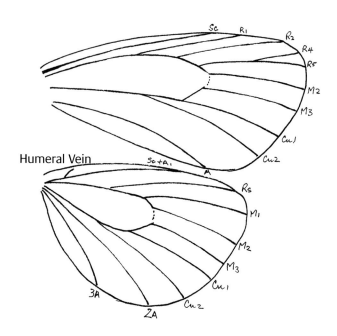

# Clouded Yellow

*actual size*

## Colias crocea

Some butterflies seen here are come-overs from the Mediterranean. They are strong and fast-flying and appear here in early Summer, breeding to produce a local generation in August or September.

The Clouded yellow prefers open country and especially fields of clover or lucerne, which, with bird'sfoot trefoil and vetches are the preferred larval foodplants. Eggs laid on the leaf hatch in about a week. The caterpillars feed on the leaves and mature in about a month. They then creep down to the stems and attach themselves there to pupate. The pupal stage lasts some 2-3 weeks after which the butterflies

emerge from early developing pupae. Late developing pupae overwinter and emerge in the following Spring.

The illustration shows the female butterfly. The male is similar, differing only in that the black areas along the wing margin have no yellow patches. The depth of the yellow colour varies and some individuals are quite pale.

*Wingspan 46 - 54mm*

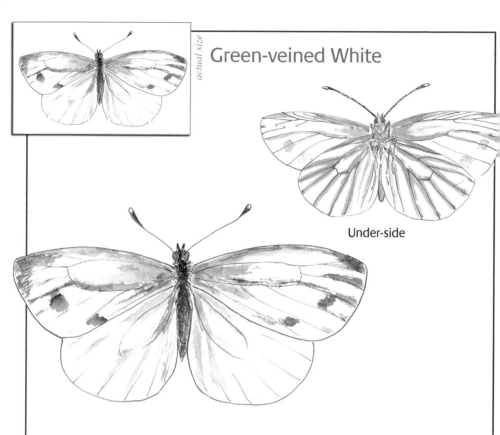

# Green-veined White

Under-side

## *Pieris napi*

One of the most common and widespread butterflies in the British Isles, found in many places - damp meadows and marshes, stream banks, hedgerows, roadsides and gardens. Unlike the Large white and the Small white it does not attack cultivated vegetables but feeds entirely on wild brassicas such as cuckoo-flower and bitter cress. Seen in the garden it is often mistaken for the unwanted whites but its size and the green-lined veins on the underside of the wings show its difference.

Depending on the weather, the Green-veined white may have one or two generations in a year and may be seen any time from April to September. Eggs are laid on the underside of food-plant leaves and hatch after 5 days into caterpillars which feed on the leaves. After some 2-3 weeks of feeding the caterpillar pupates. To achieve this it does not spin a cocoon but forms a chrysalis which is basically a tightly folded-up adult with a thick skin. It is attached to the plant stem with a cord and overwinters in this stage.

*Body length 14mm*
*Wingspan 46mm*

# Large White

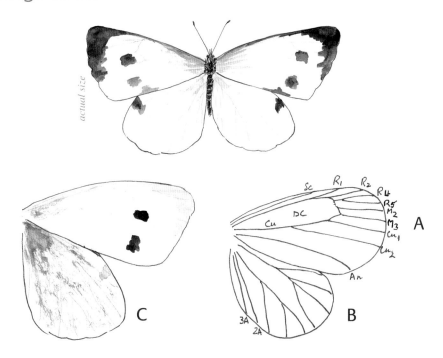

*actual size*

A

B

C

*Pieris brassicae*

Very widespread, from Europe, North Africa to Asia Minor; many from Europe migrate to Great Britain. They are strong, fast fliers and have been timed at speeds of over 15km/hr. They may be found in gardens, fields or wastelands, wherever the food plants of the larvae grow.

In Southern Britain there are two generations in the year, and adults may be seen flying from April to October. The females can detect the odour of plants in the cabbage family on which the eggs are laid, the first batch, usually of 50 to 100, in May and the second in July. These hatch in about a week. and the larvae,

(caterpillars) eat the leaves, often reducing them to a skeleton. The caterpillars absorb chemicals from the plant which makes them toxic to predators, and their bright yellow and black pattern acts as a warning. After about 4 weeks the caterpillars leave the plant and pupate, in a chrysalis attached to walls, fences or tree trunks. The first generation produces adult butterflies in about 2 weeks, the second generation overwinters.

*Body length 24mm*
*Wingspan 60 - 70mm*

**A:** forewing
**B:** hindwing
**C:** underside of wings

actual size

# Orange Tip

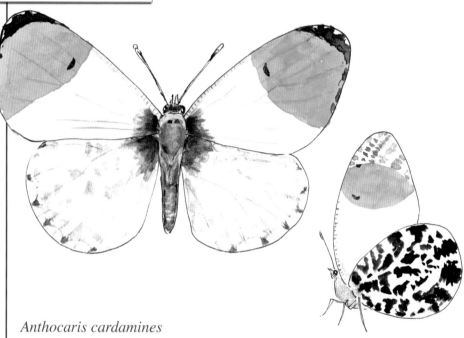

## *Anthocaris cardamines*

The illustration shows the male butterfly with the orange-tipped wings which give it the common name. The female is less colourful, lacking any orange colour on the wings, and the undersides are paler and less well marked. The Orange tip is one of the first butterflies to be seen in Spring, usually flying from April until June, with a life span of some 18 days. It is quite common in gardens, lanes, damp meadows and woodland edges, wherever its foodplants grow. These largely consist of crucifers such as cuckoo flower, bittercress, lady`s smock, hedge mustard, charlock and garlic mustard.

The females lay their eggs beneath the

flower buds of the foodplant. The caterpillars hatch in June and July and feed on the seedpods of the foodplant; they are quite hairy and produce a sweet liquid on which ants feed. At the end of July the caterpillar pupates in a chrysalis which is attached to the plant stem. The chrysalis overwinters and the next generation of butterflies appear in the following April.

The Orange tip is a resident in the Island. It is said to be declining in Britain due to the drainage of damp meadows and the use of insecticides.

*Wingspan 35 - 50mm*

# Small White

*actual size*

## Pieris rapae

A butterfly which most people are aware of, it is the commonest species in urban areas and the second commonest in the whole country. Its range extends throughout Europe and Asia and it has been introduced into North America and Australia. It is found in gardens and wherever else the larval food plants of the cabbage family grow. There are 2 or 3 generations per year, and migrants from Europe fly in, so adults can be seen from April to October.

Cultivated cabbages, Brussels sprouts, cauliflowers, wild crucifers such as hedge mustard, garlic mustard and hoary cress, as well as garden nasturtiums are the favoured food plants.

Eggs are laid on the underside of leaves in April and again in July. Caterpillars hatch out in about a week and tend to feed in the heart of the cabbage rather than the outer leaves. They are not conspicuous as they are a green colour very similar to that of the leaves. In 3-4 weeks the caterpillars are fully grown and pupate, attaching the chrysalis to the plant, or to walls and fences. Pupae from the April brood produce butterflies in about 3 weeks, and those of the July brood overwinter.

*Body length 11mm*
*Wingspan 47mm*

# Common Blue

*Polyommatus icarus*

The upper butterfly illustrated is a male, the lower a female. The underside of the male wing is similar in pattern to that of the female, but rather duller in colour.

Widespread and common,in open grassy places; males are often very obvious as they establish territories and spend their time either defending them against rivals or searching for females. Adults are on the wing in mid-May and again in August. Caterpillar foodplants include bird's-foot trefoil and clover. Eggs are laid in early July, and again in August and take about a week to hatch. The second generation of caterpillars climb down to the ground, where they overwinter, climbing up again to resume feeding in March so caterpillars are present over much of the year. They produce a sugary secretion which is much relished by ants. The fully grown caterpillar pupates in a silky cocoon at the base of the plant, where it is either buried by the ants, or carried into their nest and cared for by them. Adult butterflies are on the wing from mid-May to June and August to October, their lifespan around 3 weeks. They live in colonies of 100-200, by day they fly low over the ground and by night they roost head downwards, communally, on tall grass clumps.

*Wingspan 25 - 40mm*

# Holly Blue

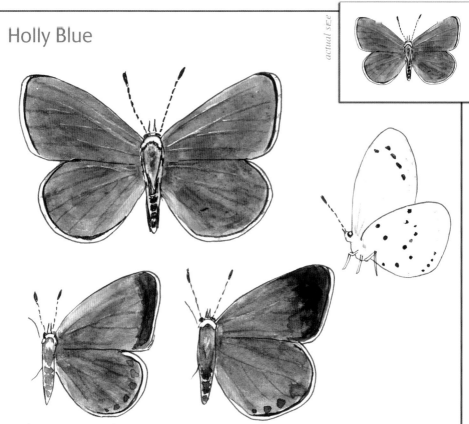

*Celastrina argiolus*

The upper butterfly is a male. The lower one on the left side is a first generation female, on the right side is a second generation female. Both of these have a black band on the outer edge of the forewing. That of the a second generation female is more than twice as wide as that of the first, and the upper edge of the hind wing is dark.

It is unusual in having two separate larval foodplants, holly and ivy, which support the two generations. Eggs are laid on Holly in May to produce the first generation of butterflies in July. These lay their eggs in Autumn on the ivy buds and the caterpillars feed for three weeks then pupate and pass the Winter as a chrysalis on the ground. Butterflies emerge in the following April.

The caterpillars produce a sweet secretion that is attractive to ants, which in return, protect the caterpillars during pupation.

*Wingspan 26 - 35mm*

# Small Copper

*Lycaena phlaeas*

Widespread and common throughout Europe, in grasslands, roadside verges and gardens where the foodplants, docks and sorrel grow. Numbers fluctuate from year to year. Some decrease is due to loss of habitat with increased agricultural use of the land, some is due to weather as the butterfly will only lay eggs when the sun is shining, so numbers decrease in seasons when dull weather predominates

The Small Copper has two, and sometimes three generations per year. Eggs are laid in May and July at the base of the leaf on the midrib of the food plant. The caterpillars hatch out in about one week  and feed on the underside of the leaves. In feeding they leave the epidermis of the leaf upper surface intact so their feeding paths are marked out by transparent lines. Summer caterpillars are full grown in about 4 weeks and pupate on the underside of the leaves. Adults emerge in 3-4 weeks. Caterpillars of the July brood overwinter and complete their growth in the following Spring.

*Body length 10mm*
*Wingspan 32 - 35mm*

# Family Nymphalidae

A large family of medium to large sized butterflies containing many of the most colourful and easily recognised garden species. Sometimes known as "brush-footed butterflies" or "four-footed-butterflies" because the forelegs are very small, not used for walking, and covered with tufts of hairy scales. The vein pattern shows veins R3, R4 and R5, and sometimes also R2 in the forewing arising from a common stalk.

The family is often divided into five or six subfamilies. The butterflies depicted here fall into two subfamilies: the Nymphalinae (Peacock, Red Admiral, Painted Lady, Small Tortoiseshell, Dark Green Fritillary and Comma) and the Satyrinae (Grayling, Small Heath, Speckled Wood, Meadow Brown and Wall Brown). These are more usually designated as a separate family, **the Satyridae**

In the Nymphalinae the humeral vein is present in the hindwing, but in the Satyrinae it is often reduced. The forewing in the Satyrinae differs in that the base of vein Sc and sometimes also Cu is markedly swollen. The diagram below shows these features.

Wing veins

| | |
|---|---|
| Sc | subcostal |
| R | radial |
| M | medial |
| Cu | cubital |
| A | anal |

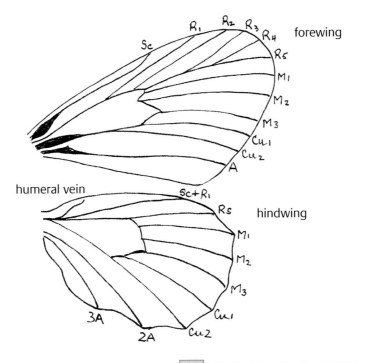

# Comma

## *Polygonia c-album*

A butterfly which is easily recognised by its  scalloped wings. The hind underwing shows the white comma-shaped mark which has given rise to its common name. When the wings are closed they look like dead leaves. This is excellent camouflage for a butterfly that overwinters as an adult, resting on tree branches.

In Spring the first generation butterflies, which have overwintered, mate, and lay their eggs on hop, nettle or elm leaves in April. In May, these hatch to caterpillars which also are camouflaged as they resemble bird droppings. These caterpillars pupate for some two weeks in June and adults of the second generation emerge in July. They have a life of about four weeks, during which time they lay eggs which hatch in mid-July, pupate in August and give rise in September to the adult butterflies that will overwinter.  The illustration shows a second generation male; females are similar but the wings are somewhat lighter in colour and the margins tend to be less scalloped.

*Wing span 44 - 48mm*

# Dark Green Fritillary

actual size

*Argynnis aglaja*

This butterfly has a wide range of habitats including coastal cliffs, moorland, dunes, grassland and hilly areas, provided the larval foodplants, violets are present.

Adult butterflies usually live within fairly large, colonies; they are fast and powerful flyers and are usually seen in ones and twos, feeding on the nectar of thistle flowers.

Eggs are laid on leaves and stems of violets in August and the caterpillars emerge about 17 days later. They feed on leaves then overwinter, emerging from their hibernation in March when they continue to feed until May. They

then pupate in the dense vegetation at the base of the plants. The butterflies emerge in mid-June with a life expectancy of some 6 - 8 weeks.

The illustration shows a male, the female is similar but the colour is often paler.

*Wing span quoted is variable, outside limits 48 - 69mm*

*In some texts Argynnis aglaja is called Mesoacidalia aglaja*

117

# Painted Lady

*actual size*

## Cynthia cardui

The breeding population of the Painted lady is situated in southern Europe and North Africa, butterflies seen in the British Isles are all migrants from these areas. Numbers depend on weather conditions en route.

There may be two generations per year depending on the time of arrival of the first migrants.

The habitat is open countryside and rough meadowland, where they can find  their food plants, which are thistles, nettles, mallow, burdock and possibly others. Eggs are laid on the food plant on the upper surface of leaves in June and August, and these hatch in about one week. The caterpillars construct a tent of leaves joined with spun silk, and feed within it, becoming fully grown in 3-4 weeks. Pupation takes place within the tent and butterflies emerge after some 2 weeks. These butterflies will lay eggs in August, but this second brood, like the butterflies themselves, will not survive the British Winter.

*Body length 23mm*
*Wingspan 68mm*

# Peacock

*actual size*

## Inachis io

One of the largest and most colourful of our butterflies, often seen in gardens as well as many other places in the countryside.

As with the Small tortoiseshell, numerous eggs are laid in May on the stinging nettle and the caterpillars live together in a silken web. These caterpillars are black, with white spots and glossy black spines. During June and July the caterpillars feed on the nettle plant then leave the plant to pupate.

Adult butterflies appear in July and are quite long-lived, feeding and basking until Winter, when they hibernate in groups, in sheltered places such as

hollow trees in woodland. They reappear in Spring on sunny days and spend much of their time feeding. The males also behave in a similar way to the Small tortoiseshell, establishing their territories along hedgerows and woodland edges, and intercepting females flying past.

The Peacock underwing is dark and when closed the butterfly is almost invisible against a dark background. Again, this is an effective camouflage against would-be predators.

*Body length 22mm*
*Wingspan 67mm*

# Red Admiral

## *Vanessa atalanta*

As with the Painted lady, the Red Admiral has its breeding centre in south Europe and North Africa and migrates to the British Isles. It is quite common and is found in woodland margins, hedgerows, gardens and waste ground, wherever it can find the larval foodplants, which are mainly stinging nettles.

Adult butterflies are usually seen in late May, and the eggs are laid in June on nettles which are in sunny situations. Unlike the Small tortoiseshell and the Peacock, the eggs are laid singly and not in batches. The caterpillars which emerge after about one week make themselves a tent of leaves folded over and fastened with silk. The caterpillars feed inside their tents and become fully grown in about 3-4 weeks. They then pupate within the tent. After 2-3 weeks the adult butterflies emerge. These may start another generation which appears in September and these butterflies are often seen feeding on rotten fruit and ivy flowers. They may persist until November, when they either attempt to migrate back to warmer countries or to hibernate. If the latter, they cannot survive the cold of the British Winter.

*Body length 23mm*
*Wingspan 63mm*

# Small Tortoiseshell

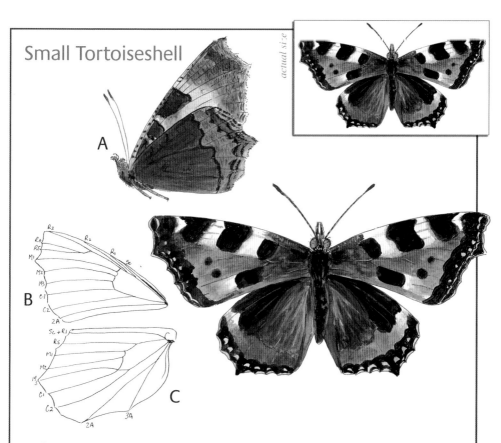

*actual size*

*Aglais urticae*

Common and colourful, this butterfly is a frequent visitor to gardens, and is also found in many other open places in the countryside. It is sometimes seen in Winter as the adult butterfly often hibernates in outbuildings or houses.

Eggs are laid in batches of about 80 on the underside of stinging nettle leaves in May. They hatch in about 10 days and the young larvae live together, in a web which they spin over the plant. As they grow bigger the community of black and yellow caterpillars in their web is quite conspicuous. Finally, after about 4 weeks, the fully grown caterpillars disperse and pupate.

The adult butterflies emerge about 2 weeks later, after pupation, and, if the weather is good, start off a second generation. The male butterflies have a daily pattern of behaviour. They bask in the sun and feed in the morning, then establish their territories in the early afternoon, mainly along walls or near hedges. From these vantage points they meet any passing butterflies in the hope that they will be unmated females, in which case mating occurs.

*Body length 19mm*
*Wingspan 52mm*

**A:** underside of wings
**B:** forewing
**C:** hindwing

# Family Satyridae

## Browns, Wood nymphs or Satyrs

Members of this family are mostly grey or brown and they often have eye-spots on the wings. This is the case in all of our five species, and is most obvious in the Grayling, Wall Brown, Meadow Brown and Small Heath. They are also present on the wings of the Speckled Wood but are somewhat obscured by the other spots.

The other two characteristic features of the family are the reduced front legs which are brush-like so only the middle legs and hind legs are used for walking; and the swollen subcostal vein bases (see diagrams on pages 115 and 124). These swollen veins are thought to contain specialised hearing organs. The forward margins of the forewings may have a swollen edge with scent scales on it, used in courtship by species such as the Grayling.

The adults are primarily woodland butterflies, with fast, low irregular flight. Some of them shun bright sunlight and many species fly at dusk. As well as using plant nectar for food, they are often found feeding on plant sap and on rotten fruit.

The caterpillars are green with longitudinal darker lines and stripes which gives them good camouflage on their food plants, which are various grasses. They hide during the day and emerge at night to feed. The caterpillar has two short "tails" at the end of the body which give it a W-shape. In some species the caterpillar is the form which overwinters; others overwinter as a pupa. The pupa is not covered by a cocoon and it hangs head-down on the grass stem or it descends to the ground below.

# Grayling

*actual size*

*Hipparchia semele*

Britain's largest brown butterfly, a resident of coastal areas but not common. The butterfly rests with closed wings, but if disturbed it opens its wings to show the eye spots. This has the effect of startling or diverting a predator.

In courting, the male takes up a watching position to detect passing females. If one appears, he pursues her and when she lands, walks round her until they are face to face. If the female is not ready to mate, she shakes her wings and he flies off. If she remains motionless, he flutters his wings then raises them to show the eye spot. He then raises and opens his forewings,

bows deeply, then closes them so that they enclose her antennae, which, by this means, are placed in contact with his male scent glands. After this procedure, mating will occur.

The female lays her eggs on grass species, the caterpillar food plant. Here the caterpillar overwinters and in early Spring climbs down and pupates under the soil surface. The butterfly emerges in June or July.

*Wingspan 42 - 50mm*

*actual size*

# Meadow Brown

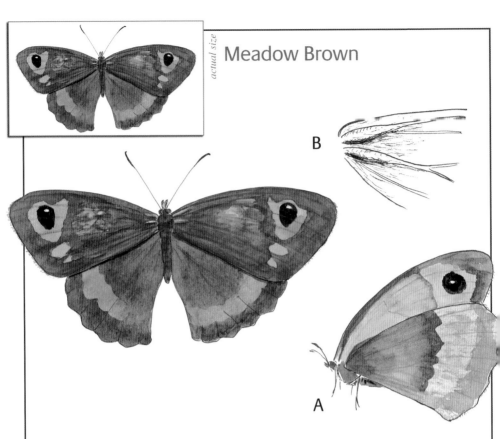

B

A

## Maniola jurtina

The Meadow brown is Britain's commonest butterfly; its habitats are various, including open woodland, grassland, and roadside verges.

There is one extended generation per year, eggs are laid on the grass blades from July to September and these hatch in about 3 weeks. The caterpillars hide during the day at the base of the plants and climb up the plant to feed at night. These caterpillars are unusually long-lived, up to 9 months. During Winter they hide in the base of the grass plants during cold periods and come up to feed whenever the weather is milder. In May of their second year they pupate in a pale green chrysalis attached to the grass stem, from which the butterfly emerges after 3-4 weeks.

The adult males and females differ so much that originally they were thought to be two different species. The butterfly illustrated is a female; the male is smaller, and dark brown with a very small and inconspicuous eye-spot on the forewing.

*Body length 16mm*
*Wingspan 49mm*

**A:** underside of wings
**B:** base of forewing from above to show the typical swollen vein bases

124

# Small Heath

*Coenonympha pamphilus*

A common butterfly, seen in a variety of habitats, including gardens. The larval foodplants are several species of grasses. Possibly because it is regarded as quite common there have been few studies of its biology and the range of its foodplants is not fully known.

From June to September the females of the first generation lay their eggs near the base of grass leaves. The eggs hatch in about two weeks. Lxarvae developing from the earliest laid eggs feed for about four weeks then pupate and give rise to the second generation of butterflies. In pupation the caterpillars form a cocoon which they attach to the grass stems. Eggs which are laid late in the season hatch to produce caterpillars that overwinter and pupate in the following Spring to produce the first generation of butterflies for that year.

*Wingspan 26 - 34mm*

# Speckled Wood

## *Pararge aegeria*

A butterfly of shady places, in woodland, hedgerows, mature gardens and scrubland, feeding on honey dew from aphids, or from shrubs such as Buddleia. With closed wings the resemblance to a dead leaf provides camouflage from predators. The male is the more commonly seen as he likes to rest in a sunlit spot from which he makes short dancing flights, warding off other males or pursuing females.

Throughout the Summer eggs are laid inconspicuously on grass leaves in the shade of shrubs, and the larvae feed on the grasses, mainly annual meadow grass, cocksfoot and couch. Caterpillars from the first-laid eggs pupate in July and give rise to the August butterflies. Caterpillars from later laid eggs pupate from September through to the following May and adult butterflies fly from the end of March to October. The overwintering form can be either the caterpillar or the pupa.

*Wingspan 47 - 50mm*

# Wall Brown

*Lasiommata megera*

Widespread in the British Isles with the exception of Scotland; in woodland margins, scrubland, open grassland and hedgerows. The food plants are grasses of many sorts.

There are two generations per year. Eggs are laid on grass leaves in May and again in August, hatching to caterpillars in about 10 days. The slender, green caterpillars hide during the daytime and come out to feed at night. Caterpillars of the May brood become fully grown and pupate after about 4 weeks whilst caterpillars of the August brood overwinter and pupate in the following Spring, the early Summer pupae produce butterflies after about 2 weeks pupation.

The wall brown is a very energetic butterfly which is often seen basking in the sunshine on rocks and walls, hence the name. Males are strongly territorial and will patrol paths and hedgerows looking for females and driving off other competitors.

*Body length 15mm*
*Wingspan 47mm*

# Inchworms, Geometers - Family Geometridae

Delicate moths with slender bodies, many brightly coloured and butterfly-like. Sited behind the eyes and antennae bases, there are specialised areas bearing a tuft of coloured hair - the chaetosema (C). A proboscis is present but it may be short.

The wings at rest are held flat, not roof-like. Typically in the forewing vein M2 is midway between M1 and M3 or nearer M1. The root cell in the hindwing is up to one-quarter the length of the central cell.

The sides of the abdomen contain large, open, tympanal pits. The tibia and tarsus are coated with flat scales.

The "looping" method of movement of the slender, smooth caterpillar gives the family its popular names: looper caterpillar, inchworm, measurer, geometer. It moves by bringing the single rear pair of prolegs forward so the body forms a loop, the front legs then move forward to straighten the body.

The Family Geometridae is divided into six subfamilies, the species dealt with here all belong to two of these, Ennominae and Larentinae.

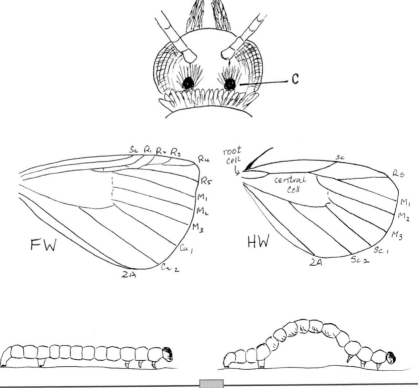

# Barred Straw

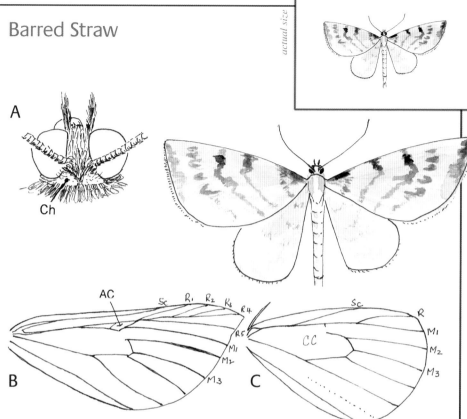

A

Ch

AC

Sc  R₁  R₂  R₃  R₄

R5

M₁

M₂

M₃

B

Sc

R

M₁

M₂

M₃

CC

C

*Eulithis pyraliata*

Resident, common and widespread throughout the British Isles, in gardens, roadside verges, hedgerows, rough grassland and woodland margins.

The barred straw hides by day and flies at dusk, when it will sometimes be attracted to house lights. There is one generation per year. Eggs are laid in Autumn and overwinter. Caterpillars hatch out in April and spend up to 2 months feeding on cleavers and other bedstraws. They then pupate on the ground amongst the plant litter.

Early adult moths may emerge in May but most appear in June and fly until August or early September.

*Body length 16mm*
*Wingspan 33 - 38mm*

**A:** Head from behind to show the chaetosema (Ch) behind the bases of the antennae
**B:** Forewing
**C:** hindwing
To show cells and veins:
    AC: appendicular cell
    CC: central cell
    Sc: subcostal
    R: radial veins
    M: medial veins

# Garden Carpet

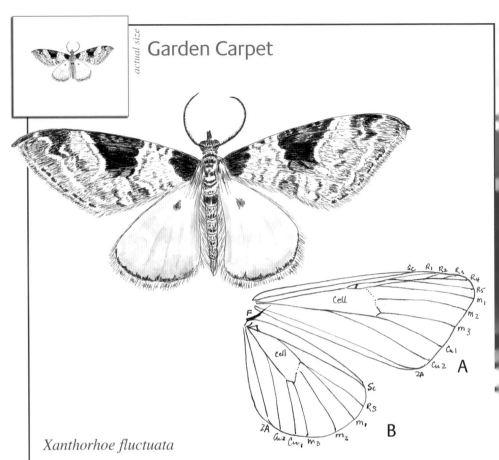

*Xanthorhoe fluctuata*

Resident, common and widespread throughout the British Isles in most habitats, including open woodland and coastal areas, but particularly in gardens, allotments and urban sites. The larvae feed on plants of the cabbage family, both cultivated vegetables, wild plants such as garlic mustard, shepherd's purse, hairy bittercress, and the garden nasturtium.

Larvae are present from June to October or November, at which time they climb down off the host plant and pupate in the ground below, spending the Winter months as a pupa.

Adult moths emerge in April or May and may be seen until September or October. There may be one to three generations in the year. The moths tend to hide during the day, or rest on walls or fences. They fly at dusk and are attracted to house lights.

*Body length 8mm*
*Wingspan 27 - 31mm*

A: forewing
B: hindwing
　F: frenulum
　Sc: subcostal vein
　R: radial,
　M: medial
　Cu: cubital veins
　A: anal veins

BUTTERFLIES

# Magpie Moth,
# Gooseberry Moth,
# Harlequin Moth

*actual size*

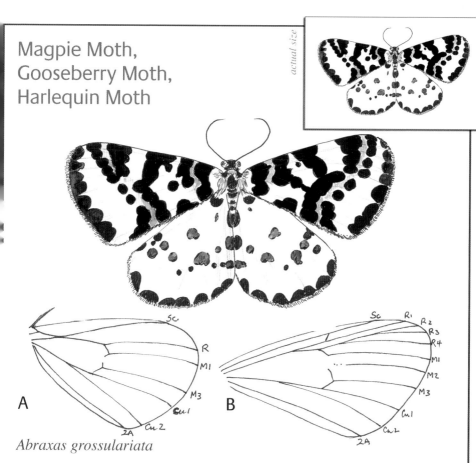

*Abraxas grossulariata*

A: forewing
B: hindwing

This conspicuous day-flying moth, with its fondness for the leaves of gooseberry and currant bushes, is not a welcome visitor to the garden.

It is widespread throughout Britain and quite common; also found in woodland, moorland and hedgerows. Eggs are laid on the underside of the food-plant leaves in August. They hatch in about 10 days and the larvae (which are caterpillars) feed until the end of Autumn, often leaving the plant almost leafless. The caterpillars over-winter and start feeding again in Spring until they pupate in May as a handsome black and yellow striped chrysalis tied with a web to a leaf of the plant. Moths emerge in July and fly during July and August.

Food-plants of the larvae include hawthorn, blackthorn, heather and other plants as well as the garden fruit bushes.

*Body length 12mm*
*Wingspan 43mm*

**A:** forewing
**B:** hindwing

# Oblique Carpet

*actual size*

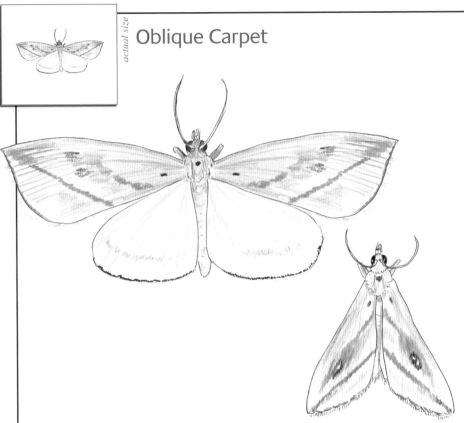

*Orthonama vittata*

Thinly distributed in small numbers over much of the British Isles; local, resident but scarce in the Isle of Man. Found in wet places such as marshes, bogs, water meadows and ditch banks, where it feeds on marsh bedstraw, heath bedstraws and possibly other species. It hides by day and flies at dusk, occasionally coming to lights.

In the south of its range eggs are laid in June and August which hatch into caterpillars in the following month. Caterpillars from the July brood give rise to moths in August and these lay eggs from which caterpillars emerge in September. These caterpillars overwinter and give rise to adults which emerge in the following Spring.

In the north of its range only a single generation occurs. The larvae emerging from the eggs in August overwinter until the following June. A second generation is not produced.

*Body length 9mm*
*Wingspan 24 - 27mm*

BUTTERFLIES

# Silver-Ground Carpet

A     C

## *Xanthorhoe montanata*

Resident, common and widespread in the British Isles in rather damp places with tall vegetation. This includes hedgerows, scrub, woodland edges, downland, some heathland and gardens.

The food plants of the larvae include cleavers, hedge bedstraw and primroses,

There is one generation each year and eggs are laid in Summer. These hatch in July into caterpillars which overwinter. In early May of the following year they pupate in  cocoons in the loose earth below the food plants. The pupation period is short and the adult moths appear in mid May and fly until late July.

The moths hide in the vegetation during the daytime but they are easily disturbed. Normally they fly at dusk and may come to lights.

*Body length 13mm*
*Wingspan 29 - 33mm*

A:  head from behind to show chaetosema (C)

# Humming-bird Moth

*Macroglossum stellatarum*

Another "come-over" from Southern Europe, arriving generally in August and September, but occasional early and late-comers may be seen from April to December. It is the only hawkmoth which hibernates as an adult, but very few survive the Winter in Britain.

In some years eggs are laid and caterpillars can be found from June to October on their food plants which are the bedstraws, wild madder and valerian. These larvae will pupate in a thin cocoon which they spin among the leaves of the food plant close to the ground, or on the ground among the leaf litter.

The adult humming-bird moth visits many garden flowers. It hovers with rapidly beating wings whilst it feeds, probing the flower for nectar with its long proboscis. It then moves away from the flower with a characteristic rapid darting flight pattern. During feeding the movement of the wings produces a high-pitched hum and the whole feeding behaviour is very reminiscent of the way that the humming bird feeds, hence the common name.

*Body length 24mm*
*Wingspan 47 - 50mm*

134

BUTTERFLIES

# Poplar Hawkmoth

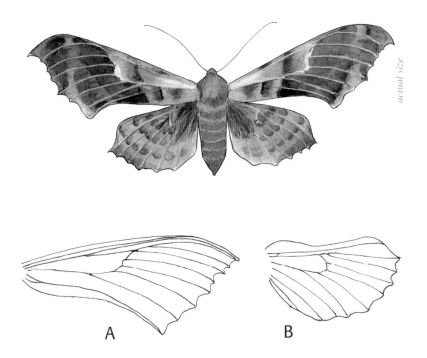

*actual size*

A          B

## Laothoe populi

Widespread and common throughout most of Europe in places such as woodland margins, parklands and gardens where the foodplants of the caterpillar are to be found. These are trees - poplar, aspen, sallow and willow.

Eggs are laid on the leaves of the food plant and these hatch into caterpillars which may be found from July to September. The fully grown caterpillars leave the food plant and burrow into the soil below where they pupate. Adult moths appear in May and June, they fly at night and may be attracted to house lights.

The adult moth does not feed, so is not attracted to flowers. When it is at rest the wings are held flat and the front edges of the hind wings can be seen forward of the forewing. The orange patch is, in this way hidden and the moth resembles a dead leaf, a common camouflage against enemy attack.

*Body length 27mm*
*Wingspan 80 - 100mm*

**A:** forewing
**B:** hindwing

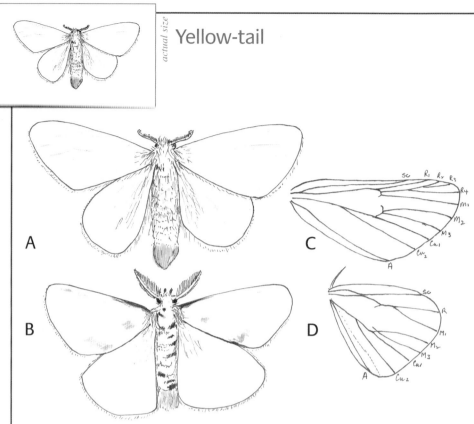

A

B

C

D

*Euproctis similis*

A common resident throughout the British Isles with the exception of the far north. Widespread in woodland, scrubland, hedgerows and gardens, including those in cities and suburbs. The caterpillars eat the leaves of a wide variety of trees and shrubs, they are particularly fond of hawthorn and blackthorn, but also often found on oak, elm, willow and birch trees.

There is normally one generation per year, with the adult moths flying in July and August. Eggs are laid during this period and hatch into caterpillars from August. These caterpillars overwinter in a thin cocoon which they spin behind loose bark on the host tree or on the

ground among dead leaves. In the following year they pupate in a similar cocoon. The adult moth rests in the daytime, usually among the leaves of the larval food plant, and then flies at dusk when it is often attracted by house lights.

*Body length 15 - 17mm*
*Wingspan 42mm*

**A:** female
**B:** male
**C:** forewing
**D:** hindwing
**Veins:**
    Sc: subcostal
    R:  radial
    M:  medial
    Cu: cubital
    An: anal

# Family Noctuidae

Nocturnal, medium-sized moths with fairly robust bodies and inconspicuous coloration. Antennae usually half to three-quarters length of forewing, simple or pectinate, never thickened distally. Ocelli nearly always present. Palpi well-developed, variable. Thoracic and abdominal crests variously developed. Forewing long and triangular. Hindwing folded, mostly plain, dull or coloured, sometimes with a central crescent-moon-shaped mark. At rest, wings mostly held roof-like.

## Forewing

Forewing with vein R1 arising arising from the mid-upper margin of the cell, R2 and R3 stalked from the upper margin of the cell, R3 may anastomose for a short distance with R4 to form an areole (Ar), R4 and R5 stalked from the upper angle of the cell. Vein M2 always arising from the cell nearer to M3 than to M1 which usually arises from, or close to the upper angle of the cell. Vein 1A absent, 3A short, commonly joining with 2A and forming a short loop near the base of the wing.

## Hindwing

Hindwing with vein Sc connected to RS at a point or along part of its length, forming a root cell (RC). RS, M-1, arising from the upper angle of the cell, or close to it; not stalked. M2 strong and either approximated to or parallel to M3 (quadrifine type), or, weak and arising midway between M1 and M3 (trifine type). 1A absent in hind wing, Frenulum always present.

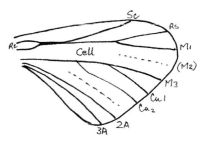

Trifine Noctuidae - vein M2 is weak and originates midway between veins M1 and M3

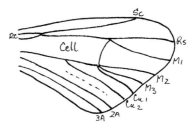

Quadrifine Noctuidae - vein M2 well developed and originates nearer the lower angle of the cell

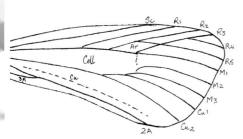

# Family Noctuidae

Forewing with a characteristic pattern composed of five transverse lines: (subbasal, antemedian, postmedian, subterminal and terminal); and three spots: (the reniform, orbicular and claviform stigmata). These are not developed equally in all species.

Transverse lines -
1  subbasal
2  antemedian
3  postmedian
4  subterminal
5  terminal

Discal spots (stigmata) -

R  reniform stigma
   (kidney-shaped mark)
O  orbicular stigma
   (ring mark)
C  claviform stigma
   (cone-shaped mark)

RC root cell
MMM    middle moon mark

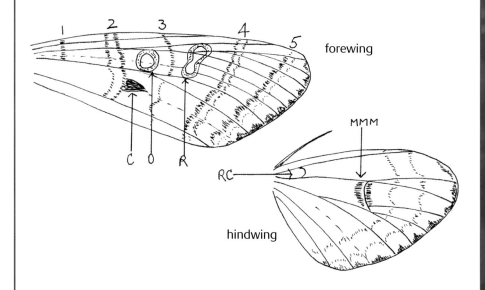

forewing

hindwing

# Angle Shades

## Phlogophora meticulosa

This moth is both a resident and an immigrant, commonly found in almost any habitat throughout the British Isles with the exception of Scotland. It is often found in gardens.

The adult moth has been recorded in every month of the year but the greatest numbers occur from May to October, with a peak in May and June, and another from August to October. The latter peak is largely due to the arrival of immigrants, often in large numbers. As with the adult moth, the larvae have also been recorded all the year round. It has been supposed that this represents two generations but this has not been proven, and egg-laying

may in fact be a continuous process. The larvae feed on a wide range of plants including nettles, red valerian, hops, docks, bramble, barberry, hazel, birch and oak.

The Angle Shades overwinters as a larva and pupates in Spring, in a cocoon in the surface soil. The adult moth rests with its wings held flat, and again, the pattern of the wings is so like a dead leaf that the moth is well hidden in this position.

*Body length 23mm*
*Wingspan 45 - 52mm*

BUTTERFLIES

*actual size*

# Bright-line Brown-eye, Tomato Moth

## *Lacanobia oleracea*

Resident and common in the British Isles in most habitats, both wild and cultivated, often abundant in greenhouses and gardens.

Usually a single generation each year. The adult moths appear from May to July, and the larvae are present from June to October. The larvae hide on or underneath the food plant during the hours of daylight and come out to feed at night. They eat the leaves of a wide range of wild and cultivated plants including fat hen, nettle, willow herb, elm, hazel, and tomatoes on which they may become a pest. When they are fully grown they climb down from the plant and burrow into the

soil below to pupate. The pupae overwinter in the soil and give rise to the next generation of moths in the following May.

The common name, Bright-line brown-eye, refers to the markings on the wing.

*Body length 19mm*
*Wingspan 34 - 44mm*

140

BUTTERFLIES

# Grey Dagger

*actual size*

## Acronicta psi

Resident, widely distributed in the British Isles in many habitats - woodland, scrubland, hedgerows, heathland, grassland and gardens.

The caterpillars may be found on many broad-leaved trees and shrubs, for example birch, elm, apple, lime, rowan, hawthorn and blackthorn.

There is one generation per year. Adult moths are seen from June to August and eggs are laid during this period. The larvae appear in August and feed until October on the leaves of their food plant. When they are fully grown they spin a cocoon and pupate in a crack or under a piece of loose bark

on the tree or shrub, and the pupa is the overwintering stage in the life-cycle.

Adult moths fly at dusk and are attracted both to flowers and to lights.

*Body length 19mm*
*Wingspan 34 - 45mm*

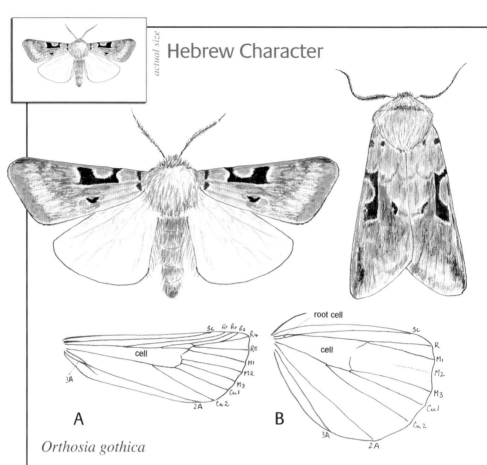

root cell

*sc* *R₁* *R₂* *R₃*
*R₄*
*R₅*
*M₁*
*M₂*
*M₃*
*Cu₁*
*Cu₂*
cell
*3A*
*2A*

**A**

*sc*
*R*
*M₁*
*M₂*
*M₃*
*Cu₁*
*Cu₂*
cell
*3A*
*2A*

**B**

*Orthosia gothica*

Widespread and common throughout the British Isles in many habitats, from woodland and moorland to urban parks and gardens.

There is one generation per year. The adult moth is relatively short-lived, appearing in March or April, when eggs are laid, and disappearing by early June. The eggs hatch in April and the caterpillars feed, mainly at night, on a wide range of trees, bushes and herbaceous plants, including oak, birch, hawthorn, sallows, meadowsweet and nettle. The caterpillar eats both buds and leaves, and becomes fully grown in June or July, at which times it climbs down from the food plant. On the ground, it makes a shallow burrow where it spins a cocoon in which it pupates and overwinters.

The adult moth will emerge in the following Spring. It often flies at night, and in quite cold conditions. It feeds on sallow catkins.

*Body length 16mm*
*Wingspan 30 - 40mm*

**A:** forewing
**B** hindwing

# Large Yellow Underwing

## *Noctua pronuba*

Widespread and often abundant throughout the British Isles. Sometimes large numbers suddenly appear in the south and these are assumed to be immigrants. This moth is most often seen in open grassland, but can occur in almost any habitat, including gardens.

There is one generation per year. Eggs are laid from July onwards in large batches, which are often conspicuous on grasses and other plants. The larvae hatch out in August and feed at night on a wide variety of food plants which includes grasses, docks, foxglove, marigold and cultivated members of the cabbage family. The larvae hide underground during the daytime and

hibernate there during the Winter. In the Spring of the following year they form pupae and from these pupae the adult moths emerge in June. The adult moth feeds on the nectar from numerous flowers, and is particularly fond of buddleia, red valerian and ragwort.

When the moth is at rest the wings are held flat and the brown forewing covers the bright orange hindwing, making the moth quite inconspicuous.

*Body length 25mm*
*Wingspan 50 - 60mm*

143

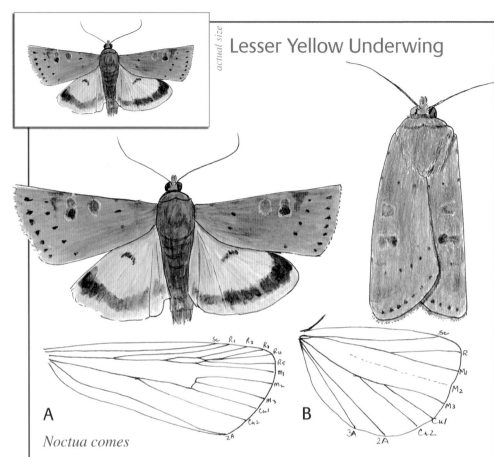

# Lesser Yellow Underwing

*actual size*

A

B

*Noctua comes*

A widely distributed and common moth. There are six yellow underwings, (*Noctua* species) from the "Large" to the "Least"; all with variations of size and wing pattern, but all with the distinctive yellow hindwing. Four of these species are common but the variations of pattern make them reasonably easy to tell apart.

The Lesser yellow underwing is not demanding with respect to habitat and may be found almost anywhere throughout the Summer and early Autumn. There is one generation per year, eggs being laid in Summer. These hatch into larvae in August. These larvae overwinter until May or June of

the following year, when they pupate underground and adult moths will emerge in June.

The larvae feed at night and their food plants include many different plant species. They eat nettles, docks and foxgloves in the Summer and Autumn, and then, after the hibernation period, move on to eat hawthorn, bramble, sallows and broom.

*Body length 20mm*
*Wingspan 38 - 48mm*

**A:** forewing
**B:** hindwing

# Mouse Moth

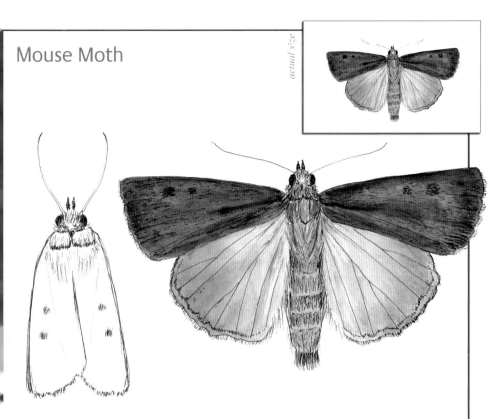

## Amphipyra tragopoginis

Common and widespread in the British Isles in a wide range of habitats, including woodland, moorland, sand dunes and gardens.

There is one generation per year. The adult moths fly from July to September, when they lay the eggs which will overwinter. These eggs hatch into caterpillars during April. These caterpillars hide during the day and emerge at night to feed on the leaves and flowers of a wide range of wild and cultivated plants including hawthorn, sallows, mugwort, teasel, fennel and poppy. In June, the larvae will leave the food plants, and spin cocoons in which they pupate, on the ground or just below the surface, until July when the adult moths appear.

The common name of this moth is quite descriptive, not only of its dull colouration, but also of the way it runs like a mouse towards cover when it is disturbed by light. During the daytime it hides in outbuildings or under bark.

*Body length 18mm*
*Wingspan 36mm*

# Silver Y

## *Autographa gamma*

Widespread, occurring throughout Europe and in parts of Africa and Asia. A common immigrant to the Isle of Man, found in almost any habitat.

The first arrivals are seen in Spring and these breed in late Spring or Summer, laying their eggs on a wide variety of plants in sunny situations. Larvae may be found any time from late Spring through to Autumn, the first brood from the immigrants and later broods from the local generations derived from them.

The larval food plants include both wild and cultivated plants, from nettles, bedstraws and clovers to garden peas, cabbages and beans. On these vegetables it sometimes becomes a pest.

The adult moths fly both in the daytime and by night, visiting many flowers to feed on the nectar. It often shows a clearly defined feeding flight just around sunset. When the moth is resting on a dead leaf the wing colour and pattern makes an excellent camouflage, in this situation the moth is very difficult to see Neither the adult moth nor the larvae can survive our Winter

*Body length 17mm*
*Wingspan 32 - 52mm*

# Square-spot Rustic

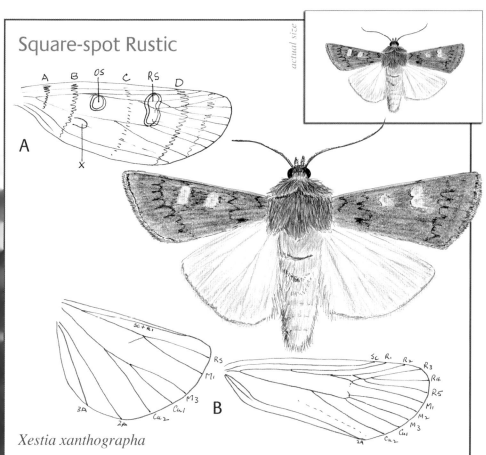

*Xestia xanthographa*

Resident, common, often abundant, found throughout the British isles.

One generation per year, with adult moths appearing from July to September. The larvae emerge in September and feed at night in mild weather. Their food plants are mainly grasses, but they may also be found on cleavers and plantains. As the Winter approaches, the larva leaves the upper parts of the plant and burrows into the soil below. It then spins a cocoon in which it lives for some six weeks over the cold period, after which it pupates.

Adult moths develop from these pupae in the following late Summer when they may be seen flying at dusk over the grassland and feeding on the nectar of flowers such as ragwort and heather.

*Body length 18mm*
*Wingspan 36 - 40mm*

A:  typical features of the noctuid forewing
    A:  subbasal line
    B:  antemedian line
    C:  position of the postmedian line
        if present
    D:  subterminal line
    OS: orbicular stigma
    RS: reniform stigma
    x:  position of the claviform stigma
B:  forewing (right) and hindwing (left)

# Notes

# Glossary

(Plurals in parentheses when not simply "s")

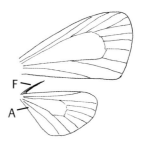

**I   Butterfly wings**

**A**nal region (of butterfly wing): the posterior basal area (I – A).

Aptera (apterae): a wingless insect, usually applied to aphids (II).

**C**auda: a tail, including the tail-like structure in aphids (II – C).

Cilium (cilia): a fine hair-like structure.

Club: (III – CL) the last three segments of the antenna which are usually distinctly enlarged.

Clypeus: (III – C) the lowest part of the insect face, just above the labrum (III – L).

Costal cell: the area lying between the costa (the upper marginal vein of the wing) and the vein next below it (I).

Coxa (coxae): the basal part of the leg, which is attached to the body (IV – C).

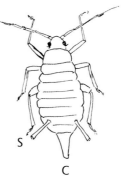

**II   Aphid**

**E**lytron (elytra): the hardened horny forewing of beetles and certain other insects (V).

Elytral stria (striae), Elytral interval: the elytra of beetles are frequently decorated with regular longitudinal rows of pits. these rows are termed the striae and the spaces between them the elytral intervals (V – E).

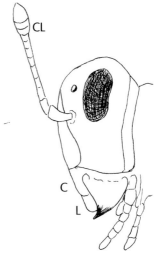

**III   Side view of insect head**

# Glossary

Epipleuron (epipleura): the elytra of beetles may be turned under at the outer edges, this turned-under area is only visible from below and is termed the epipleuron.

**F**emur (femura): (IV – F) the third segment of the leg, between the trochanter (R) above and the tibia (T) below.

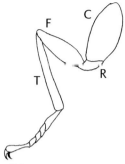

**IV**   Insect leg

Filiform: threadlike.

Flagellum of antenna: the distal part of the antenna (VI) excluding the scape (VI – S) i.e. consisting of the funiculus (VI – F) and the club (VI – C).

Fovea (foveae): a small depression or pit.

Frenulum: the bristle on the upper surface of the hindwing of certain moths, near to the body, part of the wing-coupling mechanism (I – F).

Frons: (VII – F) the lower part of the insect face, bounded above by the vertex (VII – V) laterally by the genae (VII – G), and below by the clypeus (VII – C).

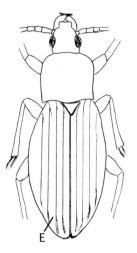

**V**   Beetle, dorsal view

Frontoclypeus: the combined frons and clypeus (VII – F+C).

Funiculus (of antennae): (VI – F) the mid-antennal segments, excluding the scape (VI – S) and the club (VI – C).

**G**ena (Genae): the "cheek", (VII – G), the area above the mandible(VII – M) and behind the eye.

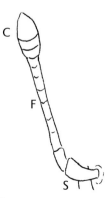

**VI**   Antenna

# Glossary

**L**abial palp: (VII – LP) one of a pair of palps which arise from the labium or lower lip.

**L**abrum: (VII – L) the "upper lip" of the mouth.

**L**amella(Lamellae): a thin leaf-like plate or flap.

**L**arva: the immature stage of an insect, often a caterpillar. It develops from the egg and finally changes into a pupa from which the adult insect emerges (VIII).

**M**andible: the jaw (VII – M).

**M**axillary palp: (VII – MP) one of a pair of palps arising from the maxilla which is one of the insect mouthparts located immediately behind the mandibles.

**M**entum: a ventrally situated fused plate derived from the labium (IX – M).

**M**oniliform: like a string of beads.

**O**cellus (Ocelli): a light-sensitive simple eye, possessing a lens but not able to form a visual image (X – O).

**P**alp (palpi; palps); a segmented sensory structure arising from the maxilla or labium of an insect (X – P; VII – MP, LP).

**P**arthenogenetic: reproduction which does not involve fertilisation.

**P**lumose: with numerous feathery branchlets.

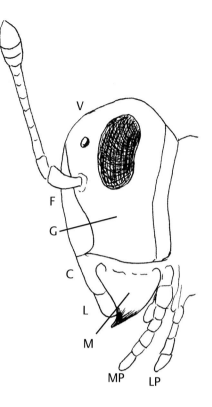

**VII**   Side view insect head

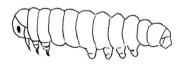

**VIII**   Larva (Lepidopteran)

# Glossary

Proboscis: the elongate, often curled "tongue" of butterflies and moths (X – T).

Proleg: one of a pair of unsegmented "false" legs which arise from the abdominal segments of a caterpillar (XI – P).

Pronotum: the dorsal surface of the prothorax.

Prosternum: the part of the prothorax visible from beneath.

Prothorax: the first (uppermost) of the three main divisions of the insect thorax.

Pubescence: short, soft hairs.

Punctate: with small pits or depressions.

Pupa (Pupae): the pre-adult stage in the insect life-cycle. Here the metamorphosis to the adult occurs.

**R**hinarium (Rhinaria): (XII – R) a sense organ on the antennae (XII – A) of aphids and whiteflies, consisting of a shallow pit with a thin membranous floor.

Rostrum: the beak of a heteropteran bug (XIII – R), or the snout of a weevil (XIV – R).

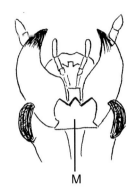

**IX**   View of insect head from below

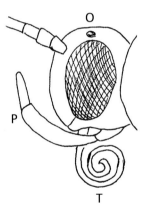

**X**   Side view butterfly head

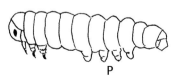

**XI**   Larva (Lepidopteran)

# Glossary

**S**cape: the first basal segment of the antenna (VI – S).

Scrobe: the groove (XIV – S) on the side of the rostrum (XIV – R) of weevils which usually receives the antennal scape.

Scutellum: the third, and lowest, of the main dorsal sections of the thorax.

Serrate: toothed like a saw.

Seta (Setae): a small bristle.

Siphunculus (Siphunculi): one of a pair of tube-like structures on the dorsal surface of the abdomen of an aphid (II – S).

Spiracle: a breathing pore.

Sternite: a ventral sclerite, i.e. one of the hardened plates which form the body wall.

Styles: small appendages on the abdominal segments, often only on the terminal ones.

**T**arsal formula: in certain beetles, the number of tarsal segments on foreleg, midleg and hindleg. Expressed as, eg. 4:5:5.

Tarsus (Tarsi): the "foot" (XV – Ft), or distal part of the insect leg, joined above to the tibia (XV – T) and usually terminated by a claw.

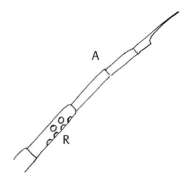

**XII**   Antenna (aphid)

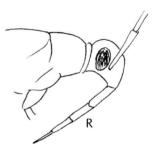

**XIII**   Side view head of bug

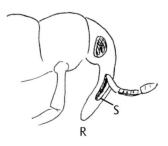

**XIV**   Side view head of weevil

# Glossary

Thorax: the second of the three main divisions of the body of an insect. It bears the legs and wings.

Tibia (Tibiae): (XV – T) a middle segment of the leg, between the femur (XV – F) and tarsus (XV – Ft).

Trochanter: (XV – R) a small segment of the insect leg between the coxa (XV – C) and the femur.

Truncate: cut off square at the end.

Tympanal pit: a depression in which lies the tympanum, the auditory membrane or "ear" of an insect.

Vertex: the top of the head, between the eyes (VII – V).

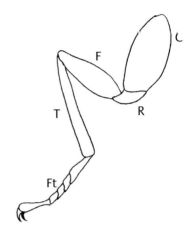

**XV** Insect leg

# References

Anon (1951) Clothes Moths and House Moths
*British Museum (Natural History), London*

Beirne, B.P. (1954) British Pyralid and Plume Moths
*Frederick Warne & Co. Ltd., London*

Carter,D.J. and Hargreaves,B. (1994) Caterpillars of Britain & Europe
*Collins Field Guide, Harper Collins, London*

Chalmers-Hunt, J.M. (1970) The Butterflies and Moths of the Isle of Man
*Trans. Soc. Brit. Ent. 19 Part 1.*

Chinery, M. (1973) A Field Guide to the Insects of Britain and Northern Europe
*Collins, London*

Chinery, M. (1993) Collins Pocket Guide – Insects of Britain & Western Europe
*Harper Collins, London*

Dolling, W.R. (1991) The Hemiptera
*Oxford University Press*

Easterbrook M. (1987) Butterflies: The Nymphalidae
*Shire Natural History No.19*

Easterbrook M. (1988) Butterflies: The Lycaenidae
*Shire Natural History No.24*

Easterbrook M. (1989) Butterflies: The Pieridae
*Shire Natural History No.50*

Feltwell, J. (1984) Field Guide to the Butterflies and Other Insects of Britain
*Reader's Digest Association Ltd., London, New York*

Forsythe, T.G. (1987) Common Ground Beetles
*Naturalists' Handbooks 8 Richmond Publishing Co. Ltd, Surrey*

Freud, H.; Harde, K.W. & Lohse, G.A. (1964) Die Käfer Mitteleuropus Band 4
*Goecke & Erers . Krefeld*

Goater, B. (1986) British Pyralid Moths
*Harley Books, Colchester, Essex*

Harde, K.W. (1999) Beetles
*Blitz Editions, Bookmart Ltd., Leicester*

Heath, J. & Maitland Emmet (Ed.) (1979) The Moths and Butterflies of Great Britain and Ireland, Vol.9 Sphingidae - Noctuidae
*Curwen Books*

Heath, J. & Maitland Emmet (Ed.) (1983) The Moths and Butterflies of Great Britain and Ireland, Vol.10 Noctuidae and Agristidae
*Harley Books, Colchester, Essex*

Joy, N.H. (1932) A Practical Handbook of British Beetles (2 vols)
*H. F. & G. Witherby, London*

Joy, N.H. (1943) British Beetles - Their Homes and Habits
*Frederick Warne & Co., Ltd., London and New York*

Linssen, E.F. (1959) Beetles of the British Isles, First Series
*Frederick Warne & Co. Ltd., London and New York*

# Refererences

Linssen, E.F. (1959) Beetles of the British Isles, Second Series
*Frederick Warne & Co. Ltd., London and New York*

Luff, M.L. (1987-9) An Entomological Survey of the Langness Peninsula, Isle of Man
*Isle of Man Nat. Hist. & Antiquarian Soc. Proc. IX No.4, p.565-586*

Luff, M.L. (1992) A Pitfall Survey of The Ayres *(Report)*

Luff, M.L. (1995-6) Beetles from Close Sartfield and Close-e-Quayle, 1995-6 Pitfalls *(Report)*

Lyneborg, L. (1977) Beetles in Colour
*Blandford Press, Dorset*

Maitland Emmet, A. and Heath, J. (Eds.) (1989) The Moths and Butterflies of Great Britain and Ireland, Vol.7, Part 1 Hesperiidae - Nymphalidae - The Butterflies
*Harley Books, Colchester, Essex*

Maitland Emmet, A. & Langmaid,J.R. (Eds.) (2002) The Moths and Butterflies of Great Britain and Ireland, Vol.4 Part 1 Oecophoridae - Scythrididae
*Harley Books, Colchester, Essex*

Majerus, M. & Kearns, P. (1989) Ladybirds
*Naturalists' Handbooks 10, Richmond Publishing Co. Ltd., Slough*

Mound, M. (Ed.) (1989) Common Insect Pests of Stored Food Products
*British Museum (Natural History), London*

Morris, M.G. (1991) Weevils
*Naturalists' Handbooks 16, Richmond Publishing Co. Ltd., Slough*

Skinner, B. (1998) Moths of the British Isles
*2nd. Ed. Viking, England*

Southwood, T.R.E. & Leston, D. (1959) Land & Water Bugs of the British Isles
*Frederick Warne & Co. London (2002) on CD : Pisces Conservation Ltd.*

Stresemann, E. (2000) Exkursionsfauna von Deutschland
*Band 2, Wirbellose: Insekten Spektrum Akademischer Verlag Heidelberg, Berlin*

Unwin, D.M. (1988) A Key to the Families of British Beetles
*AIDGAP 166, Field Studies Council Shrewsbury*

Unwin, D. (2001) A Key to the Families of British Bugs (Hemiptera)
*AIDGAP, Field Studies Council, Shrewsbury*

Wagner, E. (1952) Die Tierwelt Deutschlands 41 Blindwanzen oder Miriden
*Gustav Fischer, Jena*

Wagner, E. & Weber, H.H. (1964) Faune de France 67 Hétéroptères Miridae
*Librarie de la Facultè des Sciences, Paris*

Waring, P. & Townsend, M. (2003) Field Guide to the Moths of Great Britain and Ireland
*British Wildlife Publishing*

# Index

# Index

# Index

# Index

# Index

# Index

# Index

# Manx Bugs, Beetles and Butterflies
## Beishteigyn, Caraigyn as Foillycanyn Vannin

**Here are the Manx Gaelic translations of some of the more common insects to be seen in Manx gardens:**

**beishteig** = *small beast (usually a non-flying insect)*

**bwoid-skeddan** = *crane fly*

**caraig** = *beetle*

**collagh saggyrt** = *woodlouse / parson's pig*

**croagan** = *horse fly*

**doo-oalee** = *spider*

**foillycan** = *butterfly*

**gollage** = *earwig*

**jargan** = *flea*

**keead-chassagh** = *centipede*

**lhemeen** = *moth*

**lheimmeyder-faiyr** = *grasshopper*

**meeyl** = *louse, tick*

**milley-chassagh** = *millipede*

**myn-whaillag** = *midge*

**praddag** = *caterpillar*

**quaillag** = *fly*

**shellan** = *bee*

**shellan-cabbyl** = *wasp*

**shellan-meayl** = *bumble bee*

**shey-chassagh** = *insect*

**snaid-vooar** = *dragonfly*

**snaid-veg** = *damselfly*

**sniengan** = *ant*

**Ta ny beishtyn aym** = *I have toothache / there is a small beast in my tooth*